Professional Pilot's Study Guide Volume 2

Gas Turbine Engines

Mike Burton

Airlife
England

Copyright © 1991 Mike Burton

First published in the UK in 1991
by Airlife Publishing Ltd

British Library Cataloguing in Publication Data
A catalogue record of this book is available from the British Library

ISBN 1 85310 274 1

Printed in England by Livesey Ltd, Shrewsbury SY3 9EB

Airlife Publishing Ltd
101 Longden Road, Shrewsbury SY3 9EB

Contents

1

BASIC THEORY, PRINCIPLES AND INTAKES

1.1 Introduction.

Gas turbine engines at present used in aircraft are divided into two main classes:

(a) The turbo-jet engine, which derives its power from the reaction of a gas expelled rearwards.

(b) The turbo-prop engine, which utilises the greater part of its power output to drive a propeller, the residue augmenting the thrust by jet reaction.

1.2 Basic Principle.

A turbo-jet powered aircraft obtains its propelling motion in a similar manner as that of a piston engined propeller driven aircraft. With the propeller, a relatively large mass of air is accelerated rearwards at a comparatively low speed. It is the reaction to the rate of change of momentum of the mass of air that propels the aircraft. The turbo-jet engined aircraft is propelled in a similar manner, but the mass of air is normally much smaller and is subjected to greater acceleration.

1.3 Principle of Operation.

The principle of operation of the gas turbine engine is similar to the piston engine in that there are induction, compression, ignition, and expansion, and exhaust. However, these are continuous processes and not intermittent as in the piston engine. Fig.1-1 illustrates the principle of operation from which it will be seen:

(a) that air is drawn in through the intake 'A' by a compressor 'B' which is attached to the main shaft 'C'.

(b) at the other end of the shaft the turbine 'D' is attached.

(c) air drawn through the intake by the compressor will increase in pressure, temperature and velocity as it passes through the compressor stage of the engine.

(d) air leaves the compressor and passes to the diffuser 'E', which converts the velocity energy to pressure energy.

(e) on leaving the diffuser the air passes into the combustion chambers 'H'. Of the total mass of air passing to the combustion chambers approximately 25 per cent, known as primary air enters the flame tubes through the flame tube orifice 'G'.

(f) the remainder of the air, passes along the outside of the flame tubes, entering through dilution holes 'J' in the side of the tubes.

(g) each combustion chamber is provided with a burner containing a swirl type atomiser, and through the atomiser fuel is injected under pressure by the fuel pump into the combustion chamber, where it mixes as fine droplets with the incoming primary air.

(h) the combustible mixture formed is ignited by igniters in two or three of the combustion chambers. On completion of the starting cycle the igniters are cut off. At this stage the engine is said to "light up" and from this point combustion is continuous and the pressure in the combustion chamber for a given fuel flow is constant.

(i) the remaining secondary air, which passes through the dilution holes into the flame tube, mixes with the main mass of burning gas and cools it sufficiently to allow it to pass through the turbine at a temperature within the safe limits of the turbine material.

(j) within the combustion chamber owing to the added heat energy of the fuel, the gas not only rises in temperature but also increases in volume.

(k) after passing through the combustion chambers the hot gases enter the nozzle guide vanes 'K' which direct them at increased velocity on to the turbine blades, causing the turbine disc 'D' to rotate and so drive the compressor.

(l) of the total energy approximately 60 per cent is used to drive the compressor, so that there is a considerable drop in gas pressure and temperature across the turbine.

(m) the remaining energy, about 40 per cent, after driving the turbine and compressor is used to form a high speed jet, which has a substantial residual pressure; this jet passes into the exhaust cone 'L' to emerge at atmospheric pressure at orifice 'M'.

(n) the jet not only has kinetic energy owing to its velocity but also has considerable heat energy. The heat energy is released to atmosphere, however, and is consequently wasted.

1.4 Thrust and Propulsive Efficiency.

An aircraft is propelled by a force known as 'thrust', this force being necessary to accelerate the aircraft and balance the drag. Piston engines are rated in horse power and turbo-jet engines are rated by the amount of static thrust they produce. An aircraft that flies and is self propelled acquires propulsion by displacing, something – usually a mass of the supporting medium – in the opposite direction. To make this mass move backwards it is necessary to exert a rearwards acting push on it, consequently, in accordance with Newton's third law, an equal and opposite forward reaction is set up. This forward acting force is 'thrust'.

The simple relationship between the force applied to a body, its mass, and the resulting acceleration that it experiences can be stated as:

$$\text{FORCE} = \text{MASS} \times \text{ACCELERATION}$$

Consequently the thrust experienced by an aircraft depends on the mass of air passing through the propeller disc or jet pipe in unit time and the rate at which its velocity is changed.

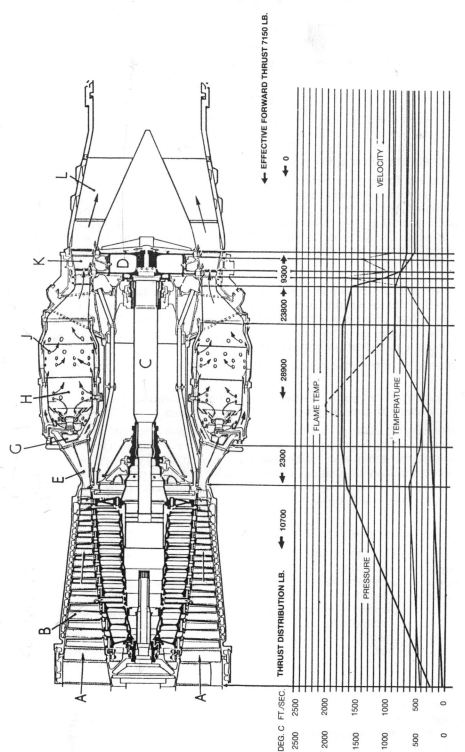

Fig. 1-1. The Gas Turbine.

It is also essential to remember:

MASS

is usually defined as the quantity of matter contained in a body and is constant.

WEIGHT

whereas the weight of a body is the gravitational force attracting it towards the earth, and is not constant, decreasing as distance from the earth's centre increases. Therefore the weight of a body is slightly less at the equator than at the poles.

Where the force of gravity is less, the acceleration due to gravity must also be proportionately less; i.e. the body will not gain speed so rapidly if allowed to fall freely. Thus the weight of a body divided by the acceleration due to gravity (W/g) will always be constant, regardless of its position on earth or in space. This is the mass, and for all normal purposes is obtained by dividing the weight by 32.2 when working in ft lb/sec^2 units.

Returning to Force Mass × Acceleration, and applying it to a stationary aircraft with its engine running at high power, assume that in one second W lb of air are accelerated from rest to V_2ft/sec. The mass of air handled by the propeller or jet in that time (i.e. the mass flow) will be $\frac{W}{g}$ and the acceleration imparted V_2ft/sec.

Consequently the thrust acting on the aircraft will be $\dfrac{WV_2}{g}$ lb.

But as the aircraft cannot move, all the energy given to the slipstream or jet is wasted and the propulsive efficiency is zero.

If the aircraft is now permitted to move, it will take off and attain a certain velocity, V_1ft/sec, i.e. the air about to pass through the propeller disc or turbine has a velocity towards the aircraft of V_1ft/sec. Assuming that the resultant velocity of this air relative to the aircraft is still V_2ft/sec, the acceleration is only (V_2-V_1) ft/sec and if the mass flow remains the same the thrust will be $\dfrac{W (V_2-V_1)}{g}$ lb.

In other words, thrust falls off as speed increases.

At this stage a factor which favours the turbine engine makes itself evident; air pressure tends to build up in front of any object moving through it, an effect hardly noticeable at low speeds but considerable pressure will build up in front of the object as speed is increased. This increase in pressure becomes pronounced at speeds above about 250 knots, and increases the mass flow through the engine. This is known as ram effect. The result is shown in Fig.1-2 where it can be seen that up to about 250 knots thrust falls steadily, as would be expected from the decreasing acceleration given to the air. Above this speed, however, the ram effect is sufficient not only to halt the fall but to reverse the trend, until at 500 knots the static value has been regained. The rate of rise of thrust decreases beyond Mach One as a result of the formation of shock waves in the entry duct unless measures are taken to counter the effect of shock waves on or in the intake.

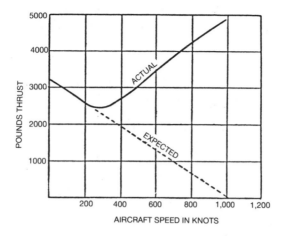

Fig.1-2. How Ram Air Effects the Thrust.

1.5   The Effects of Ram, Density and Temperature.

As altitude is increased, atmospheric pressure, density and temperature decreases, and coupled with ram air effects, these variations have a considerable effect on the performance of the gas turbine engine. At constant rpm the pressure ratio of the compressor, the difference of pressure between the inlet and outlet of the compressor, and the temperature rise across the compressor remains constant irrespective of height; however, due to the drop in density, it is necessary to reduce the fuel supply to prevent high combustion temperatures as a result of the excess fuel to air mixture. As well as the drop in density there is also a drop in air temperature, and consequently the temperature of the air entering the compressor inlet will also be lower, and therefore the air entering the combustion chambers will also be lower. This reduced temperature will allow a slightly greater quantity of fuel to be used than would be possible if a constant temperature was maintained.

The increase in temperature results from an increase in change of momentum of the gas passing through the engine, so that one pound of air now produces more thrust than at sea level, this is because there is an improved expansion ratio across the turbine, which increases the efficiency. The total mass of air passing through the engine reduces with increased altitude owing to the reduction in air density, and therefore if the total mass airflow is less then the total mass weight will also be less. It has been shown, however, that one pound of air produces more power at height, so the power decreases at a lower rate than the air density.

As has been explained, the power available from one pound of air is increased if the air enters the compressor at a lower temperature. If the air at sea level is cold the density is higher. It can be seen therefore that the thrust obtainable from a gas turbine engine is greater on a cold day, not only due to the extra power obtained from each pound of air passing through the engine, but also because the total weight of a given volume of air is greater due to its greater density.

Fig.1-3 shows the effect of intake or inlet temperature on the power delivered by a gas turbine.

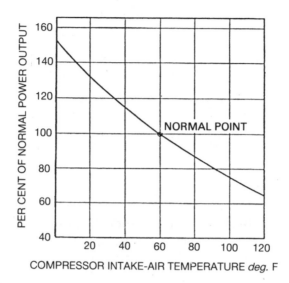

Fig.1-3. Effects of Air Temperature on Power Output.

It can be seen from the curve that the power increases considerably as the temperature falls, as much as 50 per cent increase in the sea level power is obtained at a temperature of 0 degrees F compared with the output design temperature at 60 degrees F. Therefore, with increased height and lower temperature a considerable proportion of the power will be regained by virtue of the lower temperature. As the aircraft gains height the compressor load decreases due to the lower density and, unless the fuel flow is reduced, the turbine overspeeds. In operating conditions, this contingency is covered by the use of a barometric unit which monitors the output of the fuel pump and adjusts it accordingly. As altitude is increased the fuel output for a given power setting will progressively reduce, and so fuel consumption progressively reduces. It should be noted therefore an increase in temperature causes a loss of power, since with increase in temperature results in reduced air density and therefore the weight of the volume of air flowing through the engine reduces.

It will be appreciated that so far there has been a gain due to increased density at low temperature and a loss due to the lower density at high temperatures. At altitude the overall thrust is less, due to the reduced density, but also due to the reduced density the total drag of the aircraft is less than at sea level, consequently less power is required to propel the aircraft at a given true airspeed. The reduction in drag however, is not proportional to the reduction in air density because, at altitude, the angle of attack of the wing must be increased to provide the same amount of lift, and this results in an increase in induced drag, therefore raising the total drag. Therefore the drag decreases with increased altitude at a lower rater than the density. If the Thrust Horse Power of a jet aircraft decreases with increased altitude at the same rate as the decrease in total drag, then the True Air Speed is constant at all heights, but at height the drag is less and therefore the thrust required from the engine is proportionally less; this reduction in the required thrust is accompanied by a reduction in fuel consumption. If, however, power from the turbine decreases at a lower rate than the reduction in drag, then the speed increases with height. This gives a further increase in efficiency as a result of the increase in speed, resulting in an increase in propulsive efficiency. This increase in speed also results in greater ram effect, thus increasing the compressor efficiency which therefore absorbs less power from the turbine to do the same amount of work on the air.

1.6 Intake Design.

The ideal subsonic aircraft gas turbine engine air intake, for air to flow smoothly through the compressor, should have a velocity of about Mach 0.4 at the inlet, and an even pressure distribution across the compressor face, these conditions, however, hold good not only for aircraft flying at subsonic speeds, but aircraft which fly at speeds in excess of Mach 1.0. To achieve this the intake must be designed to decelerate the free stream airflow to the correct inlet velocity over the designed aircraft speed range, and convert the kinetic energy of the flow into static pressure with a minimum of shock or functional losses, that is to say, the compressor inlet pressure should be as near as possible to the total head pressure. Total head pressure is the pressure of the air when it is decelerated or brought to rest in front of a wing or engine intake, it increases as the aircraft speed increases. As the air accelerates away from the deceleration, or stagnation point, the pressure decreases. Intakes are designed to avoid this pressure loss the intake is measured in respect of its efficiency, by its ability to maintain compressor inlet pressure at or near its total head pressure.

1.7 Intakes for Supersonic Flight.

Downstream of the normal shock wave the flow is always subsonic and, as the supersonic mach number increases upstream, the subsonic mach number following the normal shock wave decreases. The pressure recovery across a normal shock wave is near unity up to approximately Mach 1.4 and so a simple fixed intake design is satisfactory.

An example of a fixed intake, or pitot type intake is shown in Fig.1-4. Therefore a pitot type intake is satisfactory at subsonic, transonic and low supersonic speeds. At higher speeds the recovery across the normal shock wave drops off rapidly and it becomes necessary to find a more efficient design of intake to capture the airflow and regain the total head of pressure.

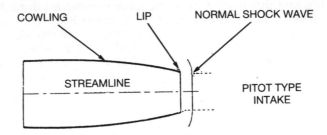

Fig. 1-4. Pitot or Simple Cowl Intake.

The mach number downstream of an oblique shockwave is supersonic at nearly all the possible combinations of upstream mach number and shock angle, and the pressure recovery is close to unity for all upstream mach numbers less than about mach 2.5. The deceleration of a supersonic free stream flow is thus most efficiently achieved by a sequence of shock waves, one or two obliques followed by one normal shock. For flight conditions above Mach 1.4 the intake must be designed to produce oblique shock waves and this function may be achieved by use of a centre body intake or a wedge type. See Fig. 1-5.

CONICAL OR CENTRE BODY INTAKE

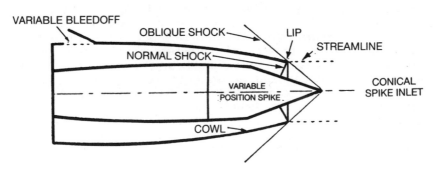

**'WEDGE TYPE INTAKE,
MAY BE FIXED OR VARIABLE**

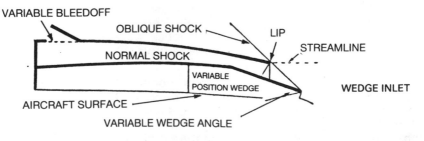

Fig. 1-5. Centre Body and Wedge Type Intakes.

1.8 Intake Shapes.

At subsonic speeds a divergent intake duct is required to decelerate the free stream flow and increase the pressure. See Fig.1-6.

At supersonic speeds a converging intake duct is required to achieve the same objectives. For aircraft which fly at high supersonic speeds the converging duct is usually followed by a diverging duct and the intersection between these two ducts forms the diffuser "throat" where the cross section is at its minimum. See Figs. 1-7 (a) and 1-7 (b).

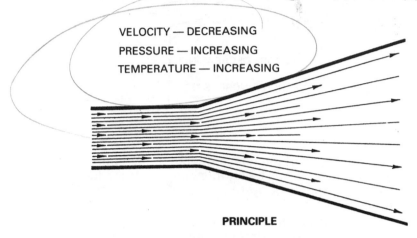

VELOCITY — DECREASING
PRESSURE — INCREASING
TEMPERATURE — INCREASING

PRINCIPLE

Fig.1-6. A Divergent Duct.

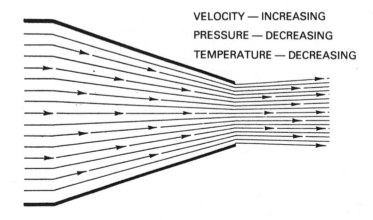

VELOCITY — INCREASING
PRESSURE — DECREASING
TEMPERATURE — DECREASING

Fig. 1-7 (a). A Convergent Duct

Maximum pressure recovery which is the product of the individual shock wave recoveries is achieved when each of the oblique shock wave pressure losses approximately equals the remaining shock pressure loss. The balancing of shock wave losses is not possible in a centre body, or spike inlet because the actual contour of the spike tip cannot be varied.

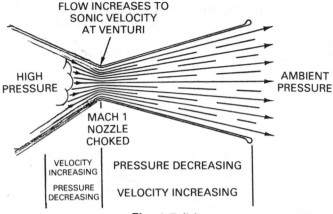

FLOW INCREASES TO
SONIC VELOCITY
AT VENTURI

HIGH
PRESSURE

AMBIENT
PRESSURE

MACH 1
NOZZLE
CHOKED

| VELOCITY INCREASING | PRESSURE DECREASING |
| PRESSURE DECREASING | VELOCITY INCREASING |

Fig. 1-7 (b).

1.9 Critical Conditions.

Three general types of gas turbine intake operation are employed and though they can be considered as being independent of the location of the oblique shock are dependent on the position of the normal shock wave relative to the intake lip:

(a) Critical operation occurs when the normal shock wave is near the intake lip. This is the most desirable condition because maximum pressure recovery exists. There are no instabilities in the entering flow and maximum mass flow is captured.

(b) If a normal shock wave occurs outside the intake, sub-critical operation exists with the shock system completely expelled upstream of the intake lip. The intake pressure recovery is less than in the critical condition due to the changes in the shock location which may cause "buzz" and result in mass spillage of flow. High drag is caused by the air spilling around the intake lip but this can be reduced if the spillage air is exhausted through a bleed-off behind the intake lip.

(c) If a normal shock wave occurs inside the intake it is said to be operating supercritically. Although near maximum flow is captured, pressure recovery is less than during critical operation.

1.10 Variable Intakes.

Critical operation can only be achieved by continuously varying the shape of the intake to allow for changes in temperature, as experienced with variations in altitude, and engine airflow as well as by flight speed. The oblique shock wave should be positioned to occur at the intake lip just like the normal shock wave and bleed-off doors may be used to divert any excess flow and position the normal shock for optimum shock patterns and pressure recovery. The intake therefore takes in the full free airstream airflow without any streamline drag at the head of the lip. A variable geometry inlet is required to satisfy these desirable conditions of shockwave location.

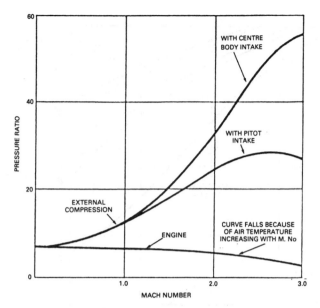

Pressure Ratio of a Jet Engine Varying with
Mach. No., and with Differing Types of Inkakes

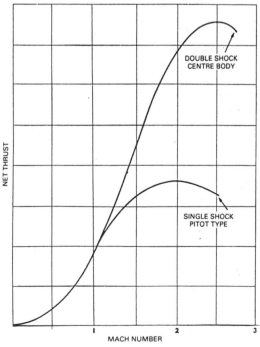

Shows how Thrust is Affected by Intake Design

GENERAL INFORMATION FACTS

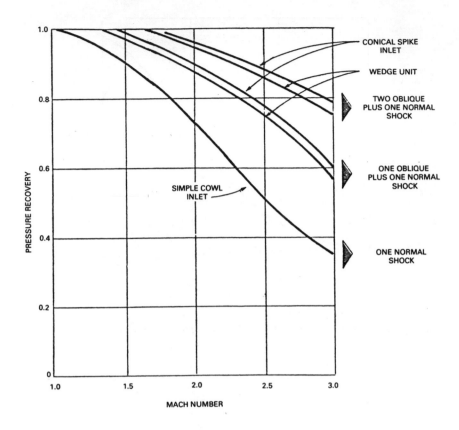

TEST YOURSELF 1
BASIC THEORY, PRINCIPLES AND INTAKES

1. The gas turbine compressor is:
    (a) driven by the airflow.
    (b) driven by the turbine which is connected to a common shaft.
    (c) driven by the turbine which is mounted on a separate drive shaft.

    Ref. 1.3.

2. After the gas leaves the combustion chambers it:
    (a) is directed onto the turbine by the nozzle guide vanes.
    (b) flows directly onto the turbine blades.
    (c) is directed onto the turbine blades by variable guide vanes.

    Ref. 1.3.

3. One pound of air at altitude:
    (a) produces more thrust than it would at sea level.
    (b) produces less thrust than it would at sea level.
    (c) produces the same thrust as it would at sea level.

    Ref. 1.5.

4. Air drawn through the compressor will:
    (a) maintain constant temperature.
    (b) reduce in pressure.
    (c) slightly increase in velocity.

    Ref. 1.3.

5. Within the combustion chambers the burned fuel/air mixture:
    (a) increases in volume.
    (b) reduces in volume.
    (c) maintains a constant volume.

    Ref. 1.3.

6. Some secondary air is directed through the dilution holes in the combustion chambers to:
    (a) atomise the fuel prior to combustion.
    (b) create a swirl effect of the mixture.
    (c) cool the gas before it reaches the turbine.

    Ref. 1.3.

7. Igniters are fitted:
    (a) in each combustion chamber.
    (b) immediately aft of the combustion chambers.
    — (c) to just two or three combustion chambers.

Ref. 1.3.

8. As altitude is increased, compressor load:
    (a) remains constant.
    — (b) decreases.
    (c) increases.

Ref. 1.5.

9. At supersonic speeds, the airflow at the gas turbine inlet:
    — (a) will be reduced to subsonic speed.
    (b) reduce or increased to Mach 1.4.
    (c) will be maintained at the same speed.

Ref. 1.6.

10. An intake designed for transonic speeds will be:
    (a) a converging duct.
    — (b) a diverging duct.
    (c) a convergent/divergent duct.

Ref. 1.8.

2

COMPRESSORS

2.1 Introduction.

Two basic types of compressors are used in modern gas turbine engine design, they are the:

(a) Centrifugal type compressor.

(b) Axial Flow type compressor.

The centrifugal type is similar in appearance and principle of operation to the supercharger impeller of a piston engine. In the centrifugal type the air flow is radial (outwards from the centre), and currently is most commonly used on gas turbines for use in helicopters.

The axial flow type has an airflow which is axial in that it flows parallel to the compressor shaft. The axial flow type is the most widely used, however, a few engines also use a combination of centrifugal and axial flow compressors.

Each type has its advantages and disadvantages.

2.2 Design.

Compressor design is mainly an aerodynamic problem, some principle factors affecting the performance being the aerofoil shape or section of the blades, the blade pitch angles, and the length/chord ratio of the blades. Another important detail is the clearance between the blade tips and the shroud around them. Compressibility effects within the compressor can have a marked effect on the performance.

A compressor must satisfy a number of requirements to achieve maximum efficiency:

(a) It must provide the required pressure rise.

(b) Compression must be effected with the least possible loss, as the greater the loss the greater the power absorbed by the turbine.

(c) It must be aerodynamically stable over the operating range of rpm.

(d) The tip speed of the impeller, or rotors, should not approach too closely to sonic speed, a maximum speed of .9M at any point on the radius being preferable.

Compressor design in most engines is a compromise between high performance over a narrow band of rpm or moderate performance over a wide band of rpm. Consequently, although it is possible for the compressor to be designed so that very high efficiency is obtained at the highest power, any deviation from the design conditions may cause serious changes in the aerodynamic flow conditions and so a loss of efficiency and unstable conditions within the engine. As the flow varies with operating conditions it is usual to compromise and design for lower efficiency, giving greater flexibility of performance and the retention of the highest possible performance over a wider range of rpm.

2.3 Centrifugal Compressors.

The single stage centrifugal compressor unit or assembly consists of three primary components. The compressor casing, which embodies the air inlet guide vanes and outlet ports, the compressor (sometimes termed the impeller), and the diffuser.

The main features of this unit are:

(a) For a given useful capacity and pressure ratio it can be made comparatively small in size and weight.

(b) As motion is purely rotary, the impeller can be accurately balanced.

(c) A reasonable efficiency can be maintained over a substantial range of operating conditions.

(a) It is very robust.

(a) It is relatively simple to manufacture.

Fig.2-1 shows the impeller of a single entry compressor. Fig.2-2 shows the essential component parts of a single entry impeller or compressor assembly.

Fig.2-1. Single Entry Impeller.

2.4 Centrifugal Compressor Airflow.

Air enters the air intake at atmospheric pressure and temperature passing into the eye (centre) of the impeller, which is designed to admit the air without excessive velocity. The air is picked up by the rotating vanes of the impeller and, due to the centrifugal force and the rotational speed, leaves the periphery of the impeller at approximately right angles to its entry at an increased velocity. On leaving the impeller vane passages, the air acquires in addition to its radial velocity, a tangential velocity which represents approximately half the total energy acquired during its passage through the impeller.

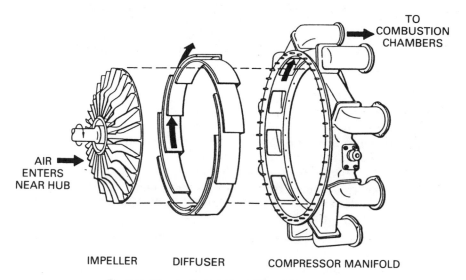

Fig.2-2. Single Entry Centrifugal Compressor.

The air then passes through the diffuser where the velocity energy is converted into pressure energy, so that the velocity is reduced and the pressure increased. Work is done by the compressor in compressing the air, and, since the process of compression involves adiabatic heating, a rise in temperature results.

Fig.2-3 shows the passage of air through a single entry centrifugal compressor.

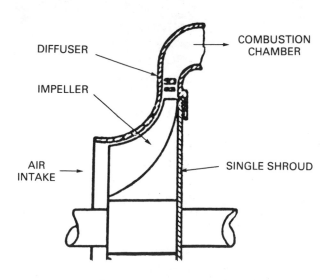

Fig.2-3. Passage of Air Through Centrifugal Compressor.

Apart from the losses, the temperature rise across the compressor depends on the work done, and this in return depends broadly on the tip velocity of the impeller and the total air inlet temperature. The common types of centrifugal compressors in use today have a pressure ratio of approximately 4.5 to 1 with an adiabatic efficiency in the region of 80 per cent.

It must be appreciated that with ideal compression there are no losses but, as with most other types of practical machines, there are losses due to friction, turbulence, and shock, and these increase with the rate of flow through the impeller. Consequently the effective pressure rise is reduced, and a constant pressure ratio with varying flow is not obtained for a given tip speed. Therefore it follows:

(a) The pressure obtained from an impeller is less than the theoretical value, and depends on rpm and diameter, and varies with the mass of air flowing through it.

(b) The work capacity of an impeller at a given speed is less than the theoretical value.

(c) The temperature rise depends mainly on the work capacity of the impeller and on frictional losses, but is independent of the pressure rise.

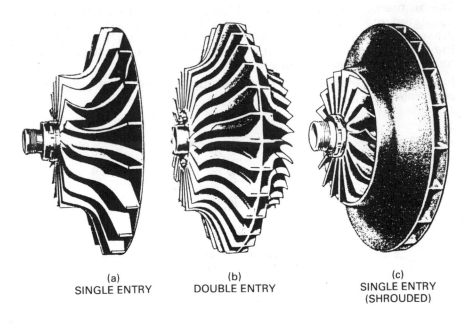

(a)	(b)	(c)
SINGLE ENTRY	DOUBLE ENTRY	SINGLE ENTRY (SHROUDED)

Fig.2-4. Types of Centrifugal Compressor Impeller.

2.5 Compressor Design Variations.

There are two main types of centrifugal compressors in use today, the single entry, shown in Fig.2-4(a) and the double entry shown in Fig.2-4(b).

A third basic type has been used in the past but is rarely seen today, this type being the shrouded impeller, a sketch of which is shown in Fig.2-4(c) for information only.

(a) Single Entry Compressor.

The single entry compressor consists of a disc having integral radially disposed vanes. When the compressor is assembled in its casing, Fig.2-5 these vanes form divergent passages, which turn the incoming air so that it is discharged radially from the compressor tip into the diffuser vanes. At high tip speeds the velocity of the air relative to the vane at entry approaches the speed of sound, and it is essential for maximum efficiency that there is the minimum shock (compressibility effects) at entry. On most compressors therefore, the pick up (air entry) portions of the vanes are curved and then blended into the radial portions of the tip, the curvature being so adjusted that the sections of the vanes in planes normal to the axis of rotation are truly radial. There are consequently no secondary bending stresses in the vanes from the effects of rotation alone, and from the stress point of view, the loads that arise from imparting angular motion to the air are negligible.

The centrifugal compressor is a highly stressed component. A major problem that arises is vibration. Vibration primarily occurs due to the pressure concentration around the leading edge of the vanes. As each vane passes a diffuser tip it receives an impulse, the frequency of which is a product of the number of vanes and the rpm. If this frequency should coincide with the natural frequency of a part of the compressor, resonance occurs and vibration develops. Therefore a process, which begins with the failure of the internal structure of the material, may spread until centrifugal stresses are high enough to tear the material, causing structural failure.

Note: Early type centrifugal compressors generally produced 20 per cent of the compression within the impeller, and 80 per cent within the diffuser. With more recent designs the compression of the air is approximately 50/50 between the impeller and the diffuser.

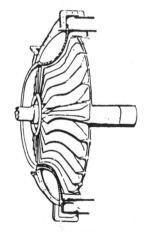

Fig.2-5. Impeller in its Casing.

19

(b) Double Entry Compressor.

The double entry compressor, see Fig.2-6, is similar to the single entry type, but has radial vanes on both sides of the disc. Air enters at each side, and is delivered radially to a common diffuser. Balance is an important operation in compressor manufacture, and any out of balance forces must be eliminated to prevent the serious vibration that might otherwise develop at high speeds.

Whilst a single entry centrifugal compressor would require to be larger in diameter to produce the same volume of airflow as the double sides, double entry compressor, the double sided impeller suffers a loss of efficiency due to heat transfer through the dividing disc or shroud. This primarily reduces the compression efficiency within the impeller on the second side of the double sided impeller.

Fig.2-6. Double Entry Impeller.

2.6 Diffuser System.

The object of the diffuser is to convert the velocity energy of the air leaving the compressor to pressure energy before it passes into the combustion chambers. The diffuser may be formed as an integral part of the compressor casing, or bolted to it. It consists of a number of tangential vanes, the inner edges of which are parallel to the direction of the resultant airflow from the rotating compressor, the passages between the vanes being proportioned so that the air pressure attains the requisite value on entry to the combustion chambers. See Fig.2-7.

The passages formed by the diffuser vanes are divergent, so that the velocity decreases and the pressure increases in the direction of the flow. These passages or ducts require very careful designing, as an excessive angle of divergence may lead to a breakaway of the boundary layer, causing general turbulence and loss of pressure energy. The outside diameter of the tangential portion of the diffuser varies considerably, depending on whether it completes the diffusion process or not. In some engines further diffusion takes place in the elbow leading to the combustion chambers. The usual design of the diffuser passages is such that the area increases very gradually for the first 5 to 10cm from the throat, the rate of increase being stepped up during the latter stages of expansion. The clearance between the tips of the diffuser vanes and the compressor tips being an important factor, because if placed too close together, the tips may set up aerodynamic buffeting impulses which are communicated to the compressor, causing unsteady flow and possibly initiating dangerous vibration. The usual clearance is about 5cm.

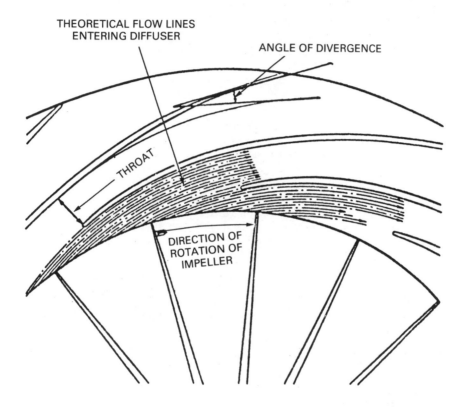

THEORETICAL FLOW LINES
ENTERING DIFFUSER

ANGLE OF DIVERGENCE

THROAT

DIRECTION OF ROTATION OF IMPELLER

Fig.2-7. Diffuser.

2.7 Multi-Stage Centrifugal Compressors.

This type consists of two or more, single compressors mounted in tandem on the same shaft. See Fig.2-8. The air compressed by the first stage, is passed onto the second stage at its point of entry near the hub. This stage further compresses before it is diffused and passed to the combustion chambers.

This type of arrangement is commonly used on modern helicopter free turbine engines.

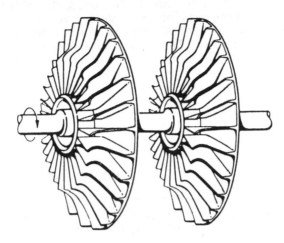

Fig.2-8. Multi-Stage Compressor Impeller Assembly.

2.8 Axial Flow Compressors.

The function of an axial flow compressor is to convert kinetic energy into static pressure energy through the medium of rows of rotating blades (rotors) which change the whirl velocity of the air, and alternate rows of stationary diffusing vanes (stators) which convert the kinetic energy into pressure energy. Fig.2-9 illustrates an example compressor unit.

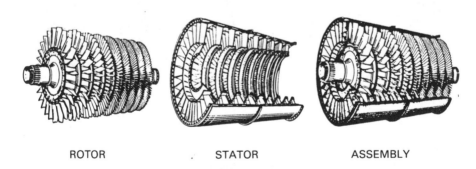

ROTOR   STATOR   ASSEMBLY

Fig.2-9. Axial Flow Compressor Rotor and Stator Assembly.

The entry section 'A' contains one or more inlet guide vanes 'B'. These guide vanes may be fixed or adjustable (normally termed variable inlet guide vanes) through which the air is fed. On occasions the inlet guide vanes may also be called swirl vanes. After the guide or swirl vanes there are several sets of vanes of aerofoil shape, or section, which are alternately moving and fixed. The moving vanes 'C' are attached to one or more drums or discs 'D', and the fixed vanes 'E' are attached to the compressor 'F'. At the rear of the compressor there is an exit section 'G' attached to the compressor casing, which houses a final row of stator vanes 'H' and air straightener vanes 'J'. One or two additional sets of stator vanes may be fitted before the first row of compressor vanes to improve entry conditions and so raise the compressor efficiency. The above is purely a general description and may vary according to individual engine type design requirements.

2.9 Compressor Rotor.

The rotors and stators vary in length according to the pressure stage, the longest vanes being at the low pressure or entry stage. To compress and transfer the large amount of air required, and to obtain a smooth flow with the minimum of turbulence and harmful characteristics, the vanes are of aerofoil section.

(a) The Curved Blade or Vane.

The necessity for the curved vane can be more readily appreciated if two points on an uncurved vane are considered, one near the tip of the vane and the other near the root. In an uncurved vane the section at both points has the same angle relative to a plane through the axis of rotation, but the root point has a lower rotational speed and therefore a different angle of attack. To obtain the optimum angle of attack at each point over the whole length of the vane, the angle of the tip section must be reduced and that of the root section increased. The vane must therefore be curved so that the angle of incidence of all sections decreases from root to tip giving a constant angle of attack during rotation, as with a propeller.

(a) Vane Research.

Many years of research and tests have revealed the main features peculiar to compressors which have to be taken into consideration in practice are:

(i)   Surface eddies which appear as trailing edge vortices at the root and the tip of the vanes, caused by boundary-layer effects through the stages.

(ii) Radial clearances between the vane tips and the compressor casing.

(iii) Axial clearance between rows of vanes.

(iv) Turbulence of the wakes from preceding vane rows.

2.10 Airflow Through an Axial Compressor.

Air enters the compressor through guide vanes to ensure a correct angle of entry to the first row of rotating vanes, where it is picked up and accelerated during its passage across the moving vanes, leaving at a greater velocity than at entry. Owing to the angle of incidence and the rotation of the vanes the air leaves the vanes at some new angle. The air then flows over the first row of stator vanes, and is again changed in direction and velocity, ready for the next stage of rotating vanes. There is now a fixed lift and drag force for each row of vanes. Increasing the lift is the equivalent to turning the air through a greater angle and consequently achieving greater changes of velocity, and thus greater pressure changes. The increase of lift is accompanied by an increase in drag, which reduces the velocity increase, and also the pressure at delivery. As the turning angle of the air is limited by the maximum lift coefficient of the aerofoil section used, it follows that the maximum compression ratio is also a function of the lift coefficient.

Each row of stators acts as a diffuser for converting into pressure the kinetic energy of the air leaving the preceding rotating row of vanes, and also as nozzles for guiding the air into the next row of rotating vanes. There is a limit to the amount of diffusion and the angle through which the air can be turned, if this is exceeded, high losses result due to blade stalling.

After passing through the final row of rotating vanes, the air passes through a final stage of stator vanes and, in some engines, a row of straightener vanes. These provide any further diffusion necessary and give the best conditions for entry of the air into the combustion chambers.

Note: The compression ratio is the ratio between the inlet and outlet pressure of the compressor.

2.11 Reverse Flow Compressors.

Some axial flow gas turbines have been designed and produced with the airflow through the compressor in a forward direction (towards the front), parallel to the axis of the rotor. Fig.2-10 illustrates an example airflow diagram in an engine of this design.

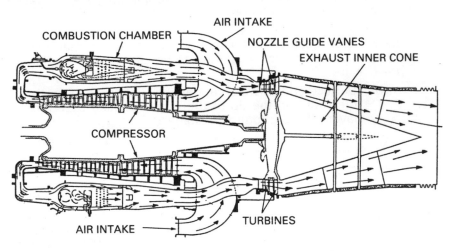

Fig.2-10. Reverse Flow Compressor Design.

2.12 The Main Features of the Axial Flow Compressor.

The main features of the axial compressor are:

(a) High efficiency and therefore a lower fuel consumption at a given power. A compression ratio of up to 7 to 1 without serious loss of efficiency is possible with this type of compressor. This compares with a compression ratio of only 4.5 to 1 with a centrifugal compressor.

(b) A smooth airflow into the combustion chambers is assured.

(c) As the motion is purely rotary, the rotor can be accurately balanced.

(d) As large mass airflows can be catered for, an axial compressor is more suitable for use in high powered engines.

2.13 Compressor Surging.

Surging is instability of flow through the compressor. For the purpose of a simplified explanation of surge assume that a compressor is pumping air into a container, and as a result of some outside force there is a reduction of mass flow into the inlet side of the compressor. This causes the local pressure in the compressor to fall, and the air or gas in the container tends to blow back into the compressor. When this happens, the flow is reduced and the pressure therefore tends to rise. When or soon after maximum pressure has been reached a surge may begin, the air surging to and fro through the passages of the compressor instead of supplying the container with a steady flow of air in one direction. The surging can become strong enough to produce a vibration, which is transmitted to the aircraft. Surge is evident by rapid oscillation of delivery, accompanied by audible indications of instability, varying from a muffled rumbling noise to an abrupt loud bang or cough and vibration.

As has been stated, a compressor is designed for a certain range of flows which may be fairly broad at low pressure ratios but reduced at high pressures.

2.14 Axial Compressor Surging.

The mechanisms of surging of an axial flow compressor are rather complicated, but it is generally accepted that there are two kinds of surge, one at low speed and one at high speed.

Surging is caused by a decrease in the mass airflow, accompanied by a decrease in the axial velocity and the stalling of the complete compressor. With an increase in the angle of attack of the vanes, the flow pattern changes and becomes more difficult for air to follow the contour of the vane, the air then breaks away from the surface behind the leading edge and the vane stalls with a sudden deterioration in compressor efficiency.

With a reduction in mass flow at low rpm, the angle of attack of the first low pressure stages is greater than that of the high pressure stages, so that the low pressure stages are the first to stall, the succeeding stages not necessarily being affected. This is often indicated by an audible rumbling and a higher than normal jet pipe temperature. With a further reduction in mass flow, caused by either a reduction in indicated air speed or an attempt to accelerate the engine, the remaining stages stall in succession, unless the first stage stall so disturbs the airflow that a general breakdown and surge will occur. At high speed the angle of attack of all stages is about the same, so that at stalling conditions all stages are affected simultaneously and the engine surges without any warning. The vanes may be unstalled by throttling back fully and slowly, and on some occasions it may be necessary to stop the engine and then re-start it.

As surging is caused by a reduction in mass flow from the optimum figure, similar effects and subsequent stall may be caused by a limitation of mass flow through the combustion chambers or turbine. This may be a problem during starting as the sudden ignition of fuel tends to cause a choking effect, which momentarily reduces the mass flow and consequently sets up stalled conditions.

Similar conditions may arise following a sudden acceleration from idling speed. The tendency to surge is in general overcome by paying careful attention to the compressor vane design, and by incorporating devices such as variable incidence inlet guide vanes, sometimes known as swirl vanes, and pressure operated air release valves, or bleed valves, situated in the compressor at certain stages to bleed off excess air. On most modern gas turbines a set of release valves or bleed valves, are situated after the compressor stages but before the combustion chambers.

Fig.2-11 shows the location of the release valves in a typical compressor assembly.

AIR RELEASE OR BLEED VALVES

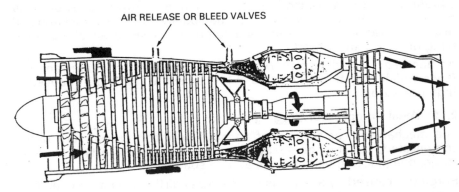

Fig.2-11. Air Release or Bleed Valve Location.

2.15 Effects of Compressor Surge.

The surging of the compressor imposes severe vibrations and excessive temperatures on the engine and should be avoided or minimised. A surge condition is also accompanied by a falling off of thrust (reducing rpm), and an increase in fuel consumption. The surge condition can be readily identified by the severe vibrations associated with it; the more violent conditions of surge are accompanied by a loud cough or bang.

2.16 Variable Position Guide Vanes.

Many modern gas turbine engines are fitted with variable position guide vanes, more commonly referred to as variable inlet guide vanes, and usually operate automatically. During engine starting and low rpm the guide vanes move to the fully closed position, but as rpm is increased they either progressively or completely move to the fully open position.

In the closed position the inlet guide vanes give a swirl to the incoming air so that the angle of attack of the low pressure blades is kept moderate and stalling is therefore avoided. In the open position they admit the maximum quantity of air. Fig.2-12 shows an example of a variable inlet guide vane assembly.

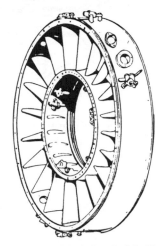

Fig.2-12. Variable Inlet Guide Vanes.

2.17   Air Release Valves (Bleed Valves).

The air release valves automatically permit air to be bled from critical points in the compressor and immediately after the compressor when pressures are at a particular level, thus allowing a higher mass flow through the compressor, and reducing the mass flow through the combustion chambers and turbine. This action will minimise the tendency to stall or surge.

In some engines the air release valves or bleed valves operate in conjunction with the variable inlet guide vanes.

Note: Some engines are fitted with bleed valves to supply compressed air from the compressor to the air conditioning and pressurisation systems. Fig.2-13 shows the location of the bleed supply points.

BLEED SUPPLY

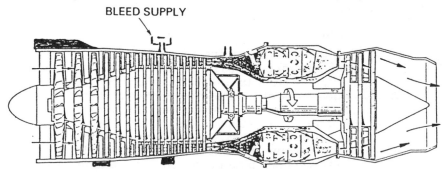

Fig.2-13. Main Supply Bleed.

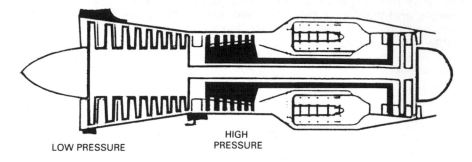

LOW PRESSURE HIGH PRESSURE

Fig.2-14. Twin Spool Compressor.

2.18   Multi-Spool Engines.

Many modern gas turbine engines are fitted with multi-spool compressors, that is to say, a single spool comprising of perhaps fourteen stages, is replaced with two or three spools or compressor assemblies. Usually each compressor spool is driven by a separate turbine.

Fig.2-14 shows a simple diagram of a twin or two spool compressor engine.

Such a twin spool compressor is a further method of avoiding flow troubles at high pressure ratios. The low pressure spool runs at a lower rpm than the high pressure spool and so the onset of compressor stalling at low rpm is avoided. Further, the high pressure spool running at higher rpm, prevents the last stages operating at large negative angles of attack. While the low pressure rotors run at lower rpm than the high pressure rotors its speed increases with the reduction of density with increased altitude. As a result, the rate of decrease in thrust with increase in altitude is less than that of a single spool engine with the same sea level output.

To further reduce the tendency to stall, in particular at engine starting, the engine is started by rotating the high pressure spool thus drawing air through the low pressure spool causing it to rotate. Intermediate bleed valves are usually fitted between the spools to yet further reduce the tendency to stall or surge.

2.19   Compressor Icing.

Because of the high working rpm of the centrifugal type compressor and related high working temperatures ice will not usually adhere to the impeller in a quantity sufficient to affect the efficiency to any great extent, and any large pieces of ice that may form will normally pass through the compressor without causing any serious damage. Any ice that forms on the intake will usually break up and dissolve when passing through the compressor. However the formation of ice on axial flow compressors can become a serious problem, since this type of compressor is more susceptible to damage from ice due to the delicate nature of the compressor vanes or blades and the appreciable loss of power and overheating that will occur when the intakes are partially blocked by ice. To prevent such damage as a result of icing intakes are normally heated to prevent the build up of ice. Such anti-icing and de-icing systems are discussed in detail later.

2.20 Comparison of Axial Flow and Centrifugal Flow Compressor Engines.

(a) Power.

For a given temperature of the air entering the turbine, the power output of a gas turbine engine is a function of the quantity of air handled. The axial flow engine can handle a greater mass of air per unit frontal area than can the centrifugal type.

(b) Weight.

From the point of view of unit weight of structure to unit thrust, the majority of axial flow gas turbines deliver a given thrust for a slightly reduced or lower weight than that of the centrifugal type, that is to say, it has a better power/weight ratio.

(c) Efficiency.

The efficiency of each component of a gas turbine engine is displayed in the fuel consumption. The centrifugal compressor may reach an efficiency of 75 to 80 per cent up to pressure ratios as high as 4:1. Above this pressure ratio, efficiency drops off at a rate which is prohibitive. The axial flow compressor may have an efficiency of 80 to 90 per cent over a wide range of compression ratios. It can therefore be seen the centrifugal compressor is not as economic as the axial flow type in terms of fuel used per pound of thrust generated (specific fuel consumption).

(d) Design.

As the centrifugal compressor is of considerably simpler design than the axial flow type, this factor dictated its use in the early history of the gas turbine engine, at that time much more was known of this type of impeller as a result of its long use in supercharged piston engines.

In small units where high efficiency is not to critical, the centrifugal type is still commonly used. It is simple and therefore cheaper to manufacture, is less susceptible to stall and/or compressor surge, and as a result is ideal for use on helicopters where turbulent airflow is sometimes a problem across engine intakes.

(e) High Altitude Operation.

Satisfactory combustion at altitudes in excess of 50,000 to 70,000 feet are normally only practicable with high compression ratios of magnitudes only available from axial flow design engines.

(f) Application.

The increase of power of the centrifugal design of compressor is primarily confined to increasing the diameter of the impeller, or, fitting a number of impellers in tandem on the drive shaft. Increasing the diameter will result in an increase of drag due to the resultant larger frontal area. Increasing the number of impellers mounted in tandem on the drive shaft will increase the length of the engine and therefore result in one of the major advantages of the centrifugal type, loss of the small compactness of the engine. As a result, few centrifugal compressor types have been fitted with more than two impellers in tandem.

The power of the axial flow type gas turbine, on the other hand, can be increased by using more stages in the compressor without a marked increase in diameter. It follows that to reduce drag on modern high speed aircraft, for a given diameter, the axial type has major advantages

It should be noted that there are limitations to the number of stages the axial flow compressor may be increased by to increase power, the greater the number of stages the greater the airflow problems incurred, hence the increasing use of multi-spooled compressors.

Irrespective of the type of compressor, about 100bhp is required to deliver one lb of air to the combustion chambers. Since this rate of flow gives approximately 50lb of thrust, the compressor of a unit developing a thrust of 5000lb requires in the region of 10,000bhp to drive it.

TEST YOURSELF 2
COMPRESSORS

1. In a centrifugal compressor, air enters:
   - (a) the centre of the impeller.
   - (b) the outer rim of the impeller.
   - (c) the diffuser.

Ref. 2.4.

2. As air passes through the impeller of a centrifugal compressor:
   - (a) velocity remains constant.
   - (b) velocity increases.
   - (c) velocity reduces.

Ref. 2.4.

3. The compression ratio is the:
   - (a) ratio between the inlet to the engine and the exhaust outlet pressure.
   - (b) ratio between the pressure at the inlet to the compressor and the outlet of the compressor.
   - (c) ratio between the entrance to the engine intake and compressor outlet pressure.

Ref. 2.10.

4. Compressor surge may be indicated by:
   - (a) a reduction in engine gas temperature.
   - (b) an increase in jet pipe temperature.
   - (c) a rapid increase of power.

Ref. 2.14.

5. Intermediate bleed valves are fitted:
   - (a) immediately after the compressor.
   - (b) at the compressor inlet.
   - (c) at an intermediate stage within the compressor.

Ref. 2.14.

6. During compressor surge, thrust will:
   - (a) increase.
   - (b) remain constant.
   - (c) reduce.

Ref. 2.15.

7. During engine starting, variable inlet guide vanes will be:
 - (a) fully closed.
   (b) fully open.
   (c) partially open.

Ref. 2.16.

8. Air release valves, or bleed valves:
   (a) have no effect on mass flow.
 - (b) increase mass flow.
   (c) reduce mass flow.

Ref. 2.17.

9. Compressor surge may be identified by:
   (a) increased engine rpm.
   (b) a fall in engine gas temperature.
 - (c) an indication of vibration.

Ref. 2.13.

10. The rate of decrease of thrust from a twin spool compressor engine compared with a single spool engine as altitude increases:
   (a) is greater.
   (b) is the same.
 - (c) is less.

Ref. 2.18.

3

COMBUSTION SYSTEMS

3.1 Introduction.

The purpose of the combustion chamber is to burn a mixture of air and fuel at a steady rate and produce a continuous steady stream of gas at a uniform temperature. The primary requirements of the combustion chamber are:

(a) high combustion efficiency.

(b) reliability.

(c) low pressure loss.

(d) low sensitivity to variations within a grade of fuel.

(e) ability to operate efficiently over the range of pressures, inlet temperatures, and air/fuel ratios required.

(f) simplicity of control.

(g) ease and cheapness of manufacture.

3.2 Fig.3-1 illustrates the location of the combustion chamber within a simple gas turbine engine.

3.3 Basic Types of Combustion Chambers.

There are two primary types of combustion chambers (sometimes called combustion cans) used in current types of gas turbine engines:

(a) Multiple chambers arranged around the circumference of the engine body.

(b) The single annular chamber.

COMBUSTION CHAMBERS

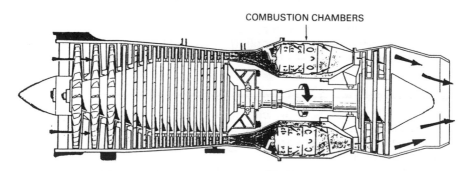

Fig.3-1. Location of Combustion Chambers.

Fig.3-2 shows the basic configuration of the two main types of combustion chamber. Different manufacturers tend to call the types by different names, some alternative names are listed with the illustrations.

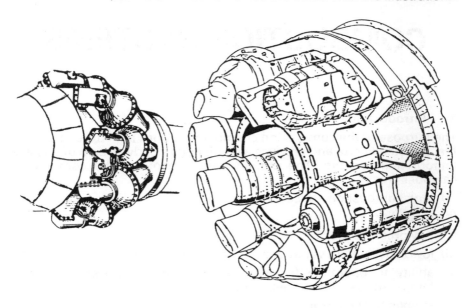

Fig.3-2. Shows a simple cannular arrangement on the left and a canannular arrangement on the right.

Alternatively they may be called a multi-chambered burner and a turbo-annular arrangement respectively.

3.4 Multiple Combustion Chambers.

Although multiple chambers, as are fitted to numerous engine types, are basically similar, there are considerable variations in detail, particularly in the methods of mixing the fuel and air and obtaining the desired amount of turbulence. Multiple combustion chambers, sometimes 6 to 14 in number, may be arranged for direct or reverse flow according to design requirements. The principal advantage of the reverse flow type is the total engine length is reduced; this is sometimes very useful when applied to an axial compressor engine. An example of a reverse flow system is shown in chapter two.

3.5 The Direct Flow Type Combustion Chamber.

The direct flow combustion chamber used in multiple combustion chamber systems consists of an air casing carrying a torch igniter used for starting (only fitted to two or three of the combustion chambers), an inter-connector and fuel drain.

Fig.3-3 shows the arrangement and detail of an example direct flow combustion chamber.

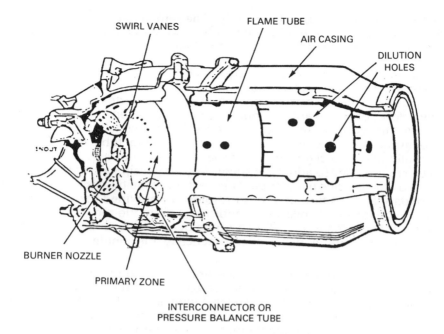

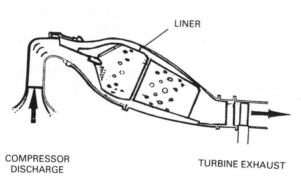

Fig.3-3. Example of Direct Flow Combustion Chamber.

In the air casing is a flame tube, located concentrically, and consisting of two parts, the primary portion and the main tube. The primary portion, at the front end of the tube, is composed of an outer cap and a double end plate, or sometimes called the colander, to which is fitted the swirl assembly. The airflow from the compressor is separated at the outer cap into primary and secondary airflows; the primary flow being concerned with combustion and the secondary flow with cooling. Approximately 65 per cent of the primary air flows over the outer cap and through the annular space between the flame tube and outer casing. The remaining 35 per cent flows through the orifice of the outer cap, a small amount passes through the holes in the colander and then along the inner walls of the flame tube, this action tends to prevent the flame from impinging on the wall of the tube and therefore reduces the tendency of carbon deposits forming. The remainder of the 35 per cent passes through the bore of the colander and then through the annulus formed between it and the burner jet holder.

In the annulus is the swirl assembly which consists of a number of swirl vanes which impart a rotary motion to the air flow entering the primary combustion zone. This action generates a strong vortex which causes a "back flow" of air towards the burner (due to the deep depression in the core of the vortex), and thus prevents flame extinction by the high velocity airflow. The main portion of the flame tube is cylindrical, normally having a slight gradual taper towards the rear. A number of holes are provided to admit the secondary air passing along the annular space on the outside of the tube. This section of the tube is known as the secondary zone. A further series of holes are provided toward the rear of the tube for the admission of additional air in the region of the tube known as the tertiary zone. These zones overlap, the air being admitted gradually and continuously over practically the whole length of the flame tube.

Combustion is completed within the first one-third of the length of the secondary zone, the remainder of the zone constituting a dilution and mixing chamber. The annular space between the flame tube and air casing to the end of the air casing. The space maintains an insulating layer of cool air between the flame tube and the air casing.

With multiple combustion chambers, only two igniters are usually fitted since the chambers are inter-connected and ignition in one chamber is propagated instantaneously to the others. The inter-connectors join the adjacent air casings and flame tubes so that in addition to propagating the flame they also equalise the pressure in all chambers.

Fig.3-4 shows the general arrangement of the inter-connectors, or as they are sometimes known, pressure balance tubes.

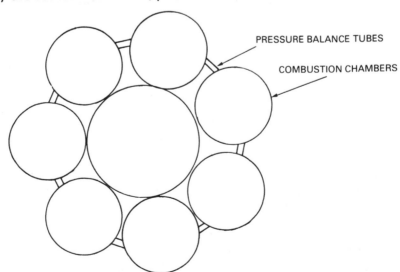

PRESSURE BALANCE TUBES

COMBUSTION CHAMBERS

Fig.3-4. Pressure Balance Tubes.

3.6 The Annular Combustion Chamber.

The annular combustion chamber, shown in Fig.3-5 surrounds the main body of the engine and is open at one end to the compressor and at the other end the turbine. Within the annular chamber is an annular flame tube, similar in section to the multiple tube type. At the compressor end is a supporting plate for a series of burners, sometimes as many as twenty, which inject the fuel downstream into the flame tube. In some examples the burners are arranged to inject the fuel up-stream; in these types the spray from the burners is not diffused in a wide angle as with the down stream type, since some degree of penetration of the incoming air is required. The air is metered and made to swirl by suitable arranged holes in the front plate.

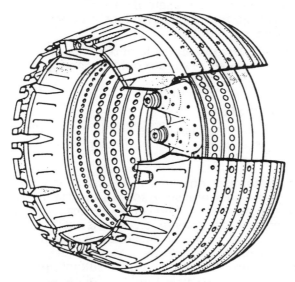

Fig.3-5. An Example of an Annular Combustion Chamber.

The annual chamber forms a continuous sheet of hot gas which flows from the primary zone to the turbine; the design is similar to the multiple chamber system in that the primary air supports combustion in the high temperature turbulent zone, and the secondary air and tertiary air cools the flow of gas before entry into the turbine. The main advantages of this system are:

(a) The total chamber area exposed to the gas is reduced, resulting in reduced pressure loss.

(b) Instead of a series of outlets to the nozzle guide vanes, a continuous sheet of gas at uniform temperature over the whole area is obtained, resulting in better pressure and flow distribution into the nozzles.

(c) Ease of servicing.

(d) Simplicity of manufacture.

(e) Smaller overall diameter when used with an axial flow compressor.

3.7 Cannular Combustion Chamber.

A development of the annular combustion chamber type is the cannular which uses a series of individual flame tubes within the main annular chamber. This has the advantage of having more rigid control of the primary and other airflows. It should be noted poor distribution of the fuel and air being a common defect of the true annular type combustion chamber arrangement.

Fig.3-2 shows an example of a cannular arrangement.

3.8 Fuel Injection and Vaporisation.

Two basic systems or methods have evolved for the injection and vaporisation of the fuel. The first method is based on the injection of a finely divided (atomised) fuel into a turbulent stream of air, the mixture then being vaporised and burnt.

The other method employs the principle of pre-vaporisation and mixing of the vaporised fuel with an airstream before entering the combustion zone.

3.9 Atomisation of the Fuel.

Various methods of fuel atomising are employed by different engine manufacturers, as an example of an atomising system the swirl type will be used.

Essentially a swirl atomiser operates in a similar manner to a water sprinkler. Fuel is fed, under pressure, to a cylindrical or conical cavity into which a number of streams of fuel enter almost tangentially. Due to their direction of entry into the cavity, a vortex is set up and the swirling fuel leaves via a single orifice on the axis of the cavity in atomised form. The underlying principle of vortex flow is that the tangential velocity of the fuel increases towards the centre with a resultant pressure drop, this results in the path that any particle tends to follow when it leaves the orifice is peculiar to its position and different to every one of its neighbours. The fuel tries to leave the orifice in the form of a hollow cone and, were it not for the restraining effects of viscosity and surface tension, would resolve itself into a cloud of particles of little more than molecular size. Viscosity and surface tension hold the liquid together, particularly at low pressures when the swirl energy available for disintegration is small.

Fig.3-7 shows what happens at the orifice of an example swirl atomiser as the pressure is increased.

At the lowest pressures the fuel leaves at a mere trickle, slightly modified by its original tangential entry. At a slightly higher pressure the effect of the tangential velocity causes the fuel to form a hollow cone on leaving the orifice, but the viscosity draws the fuel together as a continuous film which later comes together again forming the so called "bubble".

At a still higher pressure, the film no longer reforms as a bubble, but starts to break up at the edges, forming what is called the "tulip". As the pressure is increased further the tulip shortens, atomisation occurring nearer and nearer to the orifice, and over the optimum working pressure range the fuel emerges in the form of a large number of tiny droplets almost as soon as it leaves the orifice.

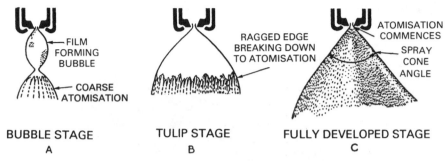

BUBBLE STAGE   TULIP STAGE   FULLY DEVELOPED STAGE
A   B   C

Fig.3-7. Development of Atomisation.

3.10 Burners.

The function of the burner is to inject fuel in a readily ignitable form into the flame tubes of the combustion chambers. Four basic types of burner will be discussed here:

(a) Lubbock.

(b) Simplex.

(c) Duplex.

(d) Spill.

Lubbock Type Burners.
Fig.3-8 shows an example of a lubbock burner. In this type the area of the tangential slots through which the fuel enters the swirl chamber is controlled. As the pressure in the fuel line increases, the effective area of the slots, and therefore the amount of fuel discharged, are both increased. This action pressurises the fuel lines at low flows without raising the maximum pressure requirements to any great extent; and it gives good results. Some trouble has been experienced with this type due to sticking of the piston that operates the variable area slots and in most cases the adoption of a simple swirl atomiser has been the general order. As a result of these problems and improved alternative designs the lubbock burner is virtually a thing of the past.

Simplex Type Burner.
The simplex burner was widely used on many early gas turbine engines. Fig.3-9 shows an example of the simplex type. It consists of a chamber, which generates a swirl into the fuel, and a fixed area atomising orifice. This design gave good atomisation at the higher fuel flow rates, that is, at the higher burner pressures, however, generally its performance at the low pressure ranges, such as at low engine speeds, was very poor. In particular its performance at high altitude was extremely poor in that "flame outs", often caused by the short fall of the

burner's performance occurred quite often. The reason for the poor low pressure performance was primarily due to the basic principle of its design being a "square law" burner, that is, the flow through the burner is proportional to the square of the pressure drop across it. This meant that if the minimum pressure for effective atomisation was 25psi the pressure needed to give maximum flow would be 2500psi. Generally the fuel pumps available at that time were unable to cope with such pressures.

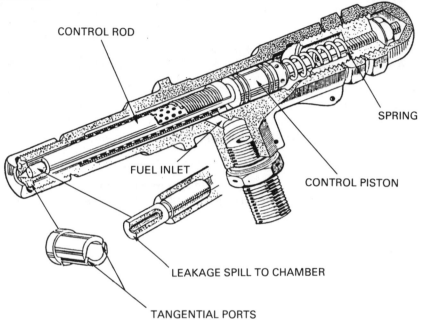

CONTROL ROD

SPRING

FUEL INLET

CONTROL PISTON

LEAKAGE SPILL TO CHAMBER

TANGENTIAL PORTS

Fig.3-8. A Lubbock Burner Assembly.

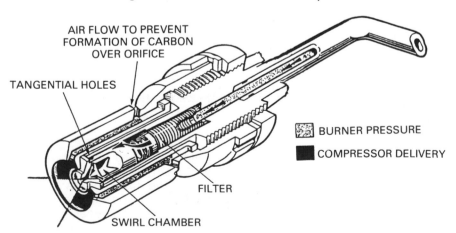

AIR FLOW TO PREVENT FORMATION OF CARBON OVER ORIFICE

TANGENTIAL HOLES

BURNER PRESSURE

COMPRESSOR DELIVERY

FILTER

SWIRL CHAMBER

Fig.3-9. Simplex Burner.

Duplex or Duple Burners.
The duplex burner employs two fuel manifolds, the Primary and the Main manifold. The actual burner also utilises two orifices, the primary orifice fed by the primary manifold designed to deal with the low flows and the second or main orifice which copes with the higher flows as the burner pressure increases.

Spill Burner.
The spill burner can be described as being a simplex burner with an additional passage from the swirl chamber for spilling fuel away. With this type it is possible to supply fuel to the swirl chamber at a continuous high pressure. As the fuel flow rate decreases with increase of altitude, or reduction in rpm, surplus fuel is spilled away from the swirl chamber, leaving less to pass through the atomising orifice. Since the swirl chamber is designed to convert the fuel pressure energy into kinetic energy needed for atomisation, the constant high pressure supply to the spill burner (even at very low flows into the combustion chamber) ensures there is atomisation of the fuel at all times. When spill burners are used in the engine additional components are required to remove the spill flow under any particular set of operating conditions, this usually takes the form of an additional pump. Fig.3-10 shows an example of a spill burner.

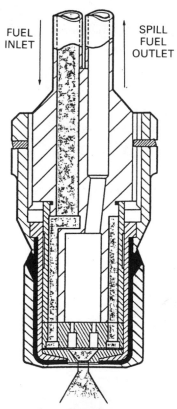

Fig.3-10. Spill Burner.

TEST YOURSELF 3
COMBUSTION SYSTEMS

1. The swirl assembly, or vanes, of a combustion chamber are fitted:
   (a) to generate a rotary motion to the mixture before it enters the combustion chamber.
   (b) to generate a rotary motion to the air in the secondary air flow.
   ⁓ (c) to generate a rotary motion to the air in the inlet to the primary combustion zone.

   Ref. 3.5.

2. The action of the swirl vanes in a combustion system is to create:
   (a) a smooth flow.
   ⁓ (b) a back flow.
   (c) a straightened flow.

   Ref. 3.5.

3. Pressure in the individual combustion chambers is balanced:
   (a) by the nozzle guide vane action at the outlet of the chambers.
   ⁓ (b) by pressure balance tubes between each combustion chamber.
   (c) through the inlet manifold.

   Ref. 3.5.

4. The fuel is atomised:
   ⁓ (a) in the combustion zone.
   (b) immediately after the compressor.
   (c) just prior to the combustion zone.

   Ref. 3.9.

5. In a multiple combustion chamber system:
   (a) each chamber is fitted with an igniter.
   (b) each alternate chamber is fitted with an igniter.
   ⁓ (c) two or sometimes three igniters are fitted.

   Ref. 3.5.

4

TURBINES

4.1 Introduction.

The turbine element of the modern gas turbine engine has either or both of the following primary functions, firstly to provide the power to drive the compressor and accessories and secondly, in the case of engines which do not make use solely of a jet for propulsion, of providing power to drive a shaft which in turn may drive a propeller or the rotors of a helicopter. In the example of a pure jet engine, the turbine extracts energy from the hot gases released by the combustion chambers and expanding them to a lower pressure and temperature. Very high stresses are encountered in this process as at tip speeds in excess of 1350 feet per second may be experienced for efficient operation. The continuous flow of gas to which the turbine may be exposed may have an entry temperature of between 700 and 1200 degrees centigrade, and may reach a velocity of 2000 feet per second in parts of the turbine.

To produce the required driving torque, the turbine may consist of several stages, each stage consisting of one row of stationary nozzle guide vanes and one row of moving blades or turbine rotors. Fig.4-1 shows an example of a turbine assembly as fitted to a conventional gas turbine engine.

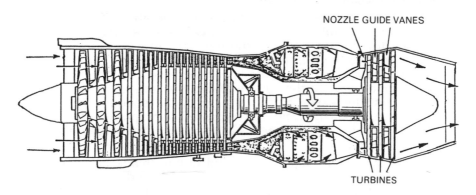

Fig.4-1. Location of Nozzle Guide Vanes and Turbines.

The number of stages is dependent upon whether the engine has one shaft or two, and on the amount of power required from the gas flow, the rotational speed at which it must be produced and the diameter of the turbine permitted. In recent years the tendency has been to increase the number of stages to reduce the stage loading.

The design of the engine dictates the number of shafts and hence the number of turbine stages, modern high pressure ratio engines usually have two shafts, one driving the low pressure turbine, or spool, the other driving the high pressure turbine. The rear turbine drives the low pressure compressor at the front of the engine and is normally termed the low pressure turbine, the front turbine drives the high pressure compressor and is termed the high pressure turbine. The turbines which drive the compressor, or compressors, are termed the power turbines, i.e. the low pressure power turbine etc.

Fig.4-2 shows an example of turbine arrangements including a twin spool compressor and its related turbines.

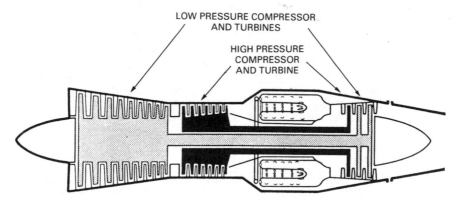

LOW PRESSURE COMPRESSOR AND TURBINES

HIGH PRESSURE COMPRESSOR AND TURBINE

Fig.4-2. Turbine Arrangement in a Twin Spool Turbojet.

4.2 Turbine Principle of Operation.

The mean blade speed of a turbine has a considerable effect on the efficiency of the possible output for a given turbine stage. This is primarily due to the gas velocity through the nozzle guide vanes, situated just prior to the first turbine rotor assembly, and the turbine blades can be reduced as the blade speed increases, and the loss of pressure is proportional to the square of the gas speed. Stress in the turbine disc, also increases as the square of the speed unless the section thickness, hence the weight, is increased disproportionately. For this reason the design of the turbine has to be a compromise on both efficiency and weight.

The design of the nozzle guide vanes and turbine blade passages is primarily based on aerodynamic considerations and as such the majority of such components are of aerofoil shape. The shapes employed are such that the turbine functions partly under impulse and partly under reaction conditions, that is to say, the turbine blades experience an impulse force due to the initial impact of the gas on the blades and a reaction force as a result of the expansion and acceleration of the gas through the blade passages. Although blade design will vary the proportion of each principle incorporated in the turbine, but in general it is approximately 50 per cent impulse and 50 per cent reaction.

Fig.3-4 shows a comparison between an impulse/reaction turbine and a pure impulse turbine.

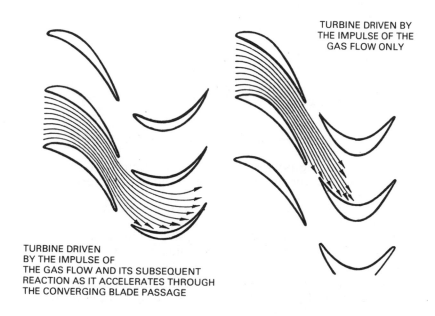

TURBINE DRIVEN BY
THE IMPULSE OF THE
GAS FLOW ONLY

TURBINE DRIVEN
BY THE IMPULSE OF
THE GAS FLOW AND ITS SUBSEQUENT
REACTION AS IT ACCELERATES THROUGH
THE CONVERGING BLADE PASSAGE

Fig.4-3. Impulse and Reaction Blades.

The turbine depends for its operation on the transfer of energy between the combustion gases and the turbine. This transfer is never 100 per cent because of thermodynamic and mechanical losses, current designs achieve approximately 90 per cent.

When the gas is expanded by the process of combustion it is forced from the combustion chambers through the nozzles prior to the rotor, where due to their convergent shape, it is accelerated to about the speed of sound, normally just below. On passing through the nozzle guide vanes the gas is given a "spin" or "swirl" in the direction of rotation of the turbine rotor blades. On impact with the blades and during the subsequent reaction through the blades energy is absorbed, causing the turbine to rotate at high speed and so provide the power for driving the turbine shaft and compressor.

As the gas passes through the turbine assembly from the combustion stage the temperature will drop as the gas gives up some of its energy, the pressure will fall and the velocity will initially fall and then increase in the jet pipe.

Fig.4-4 shows the gas flow pattern through the nozzle and turbine blades.

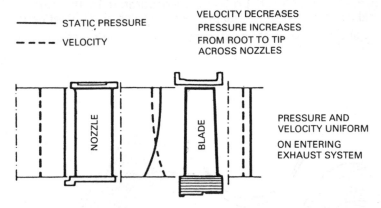

Fig.4-4. Gas Flow through Nozzle Guide Vanes and Turbine Blades..

The torque or turning power applied to the turbine is governed by the rate of gas flow and the energy change of the gas between the inlet and outlet of the turbine blades. Therefore if the energy is absorbed efficiently the whirl will be removed from the gas stream so that the flow from the turbine exit will be virtually straightened out to give an axial flow in the exhaust system. Excessive residual whirl reduces the efficiency of the exhaust system and also produces vibration in the exhaust jet pipe.

It can be seen that the nozzle and blades of the turbine are manufactured with a state of twist producing a greater stagger angle at the tip than that at the root. See Fig.4-5.

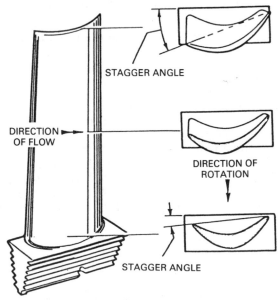

Fig.4-5. Blade Twist and Stagger Angle.

The reason for the twist is to make the gas flow from the combustion chambers do equal work at all positions along the length of the blade and to ensure the gas flow enters the exhaust system with a uniform axial velocity. Reference to Fig.4-4 shows this.

The degree of reaction from the turbine blades varies from the root to the tip of the blade, the reaction being greatest at the tip and least at the root with the mean section having a value of approximately 50 per cent.

4.3 Turbine Losses.

The overall efficiency of the turbine is normally approximately 90 to 95 per cent. The losses which prevent the turbine being 100 per cent efficient are due to a number of reasons, a typical three stage turbine would suffer a 3.5 to 4 per cent loss due to aerodynamic losses in the turbine blades. A further 4.5 per cent loss due to aerodynamic losses in the nozzle guide vanes and gas losses over the rotor blades and through the exhaust system.

4.4 Construction.

The primary components of the turbine assembly are, nozzle guide vanes, the turbine disc, and the turbine blades.

The rotating assembly, in the form of the rotors mounted on their discs and in turn the disc being mounted on the main shaft or shafts, are normally mounted on ball and/or roller bearings. The main turbine shaft may be one shaft connected to the compressor at the front end of the engine, or it may be coupled to the compressor via a self aligning coupling.

(a) Nozzle Guide Vanes.
   The aerofoil shape of the nozzle guide vanes and the blade passage between the adjacent vanes forms a convergent duct. They are located in the turbine casing by one of several methods all of which allow for expansion.

   The nozzle guide vanes are subjected to very high thermal stresses and gas loads and they are usually made hollow. The hollow space within the blade is utilised to pass cooling air through the blades which is delivered from the engine compressor.

   Fig.4-6 displays the attachment arrangement of the blades to the disc and the cooling air flow.

(b) Turbine Disc.
   The turbine disc is forged and then machined with an integral shaft or flange on to which the shaft may be bolted. It also has provisions for the attachment of the turbine blades. To limit the effect of heat conduction from the turbine blades to the disc a flow of cooling air is passed across both sides of each disc.

(c) Turbine Blades.
   The turbine blades are basically of an aerofoil shape. Unlike the compressor blades, the profiles of the blades do not follow a particular class of aerofoil shape. The shape of the turbine blade is aimed to provide passages between the adjacent blades which give a steady acceleration of the gas flow up to the "throat" where the

area is least and the velocity reaches that required at exit to produce the required degree of reaction.

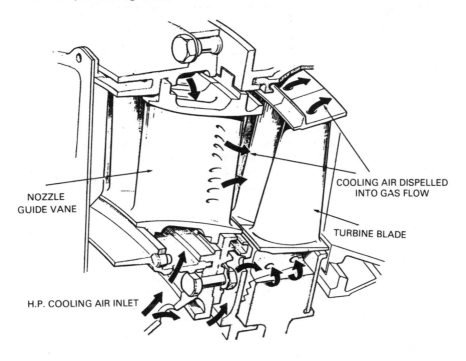

NOZZLE GUIDE VANE

COOLING AIR DISPELLED INTO GAS FLOW

TURBINE BLADE

H.P. COOLING AIR INLET

Fig.4-6. Blade Attachment and Blade Cooling.

The cross sectional area of each blade is determined by the permitted stress in the material used and by the size of cooling holes or ducts. In order to achieve high efficiency the trailing edges of the blades are required to be thin, this however would normally result in the blades cracking due to high temperature variations during engine starting and stopping, as a result a degree of compromise has to be used. The methods employed of attaching the blades to the disc is of the utmost importance. Various methods have been employed in an attempt to overcome the stress and high temperatures experienced by the blades and this also results in a limiting factor on the rim speed.

Fig.4-7 shows three methods that have been used to attach the blades to the disc.

The type of attachment that has most commonly been used on modern gas turbines is the "Fir Tree" method. This type of attachment involves very accurate machining to ensure that the loading is equally shared by all the serrations. The blade is free in the serrations when the engine is stationary and is stiffened in the root by centrifugal force when the turbine is rotating.

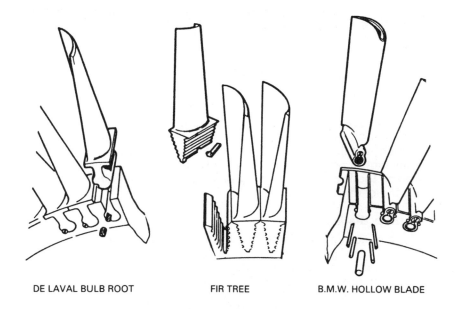

| DE LAVAL BULB ROOT | FIR TREE | B.M.W. HOLLOW BLADE |

Fig.4-7. Blade Attachment Methods.

4.5 Reduction in Loss of Efficiency.

Loss of efficiency occurs across the blade tips of the turbine and to combat this problem shrouds are fitted to the tips of the blades. The shrouds are formed by forging a small segment at the tip of each individual blade and when assembled on the disc form a continuous peripheral ring around the blade tips. Fig.4-8 shows examples of turbine blade shrouding.

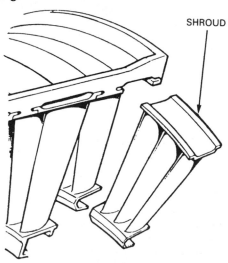

SHROUD

Fig.4-8. Blade Shrouding.

The shrouding of some turbine blades is achieved by the manufacture and installation of the turbine blades in groups of three or four blades, complete with their respective shrouds.

4.6 Compressor and Turbine Matching.

It is very important that the flow characteristics of the turbine must be matched with the compressor in order maximum efficiency may be obtained and associated engine performance may be maximised. If the compressor and turbine are not matched this may result in too high a flow which would cause the compressor to choke and a loss of efficiency would occur very rapidly. Similarly, if the nozzle guide vanes are allowed too low a maximum flow then a back pressure may build up causing the compressor to surge.

4.7 Turbine Blade Creep.

One of the major limiting factors to higher turbine entry temperatures is the effects of the gas temperature on the nozzle guide vanes and the turbine blades, and the tensile stress imparted on to the turbine disc and blades by the high rotational speeds. The high stresses imparted on the component parts of the turbine assembly make it necessary to restrict the turbine entry temperature so that the various components may do their very arduous job, and to do it for a reasonable working life.

Due to the combination of high rotational speeds, setting up considerable centrifugal force, coupled with very high temperatures the result is the blades begin to "creep". In other words, "creep" is the action of the blades stretching due to the high temperatures and centrifugal force.

If such blade creep is allowed to continue unchecked, firstly, the tips of the blades will foul the outer casing, and/or stretch to the point when the blades fracture.

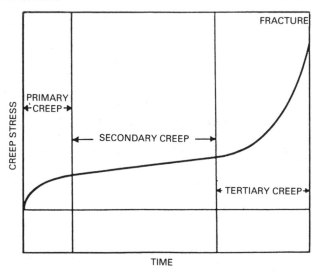

Fig.4-9. Stages of Blade Creep.

A number of points must be considered when designing the turbine blades and their associated components. During normal operation the blades will glow red hot and must be strong enough to withstand the centrifugal force on them at the high rotational speeds. A blade weighing only two ounces may exert a load of over two tons at maximum speed and it must withstand the high bending loads applied by the gas to produce the many thousands of turbine horse-power to drive the compressor. Blades must be resistant to fatigue and thermal shock, so they will not fail under the influence of high frequency fluctuations in the gas flow conditions, and finally they must be resistant to corrosion and oxidation.

Fig.4-9 shows a graph of the three basic stages of "creep" and ultimately, if the blades are not changed, their subsequent fracture.

On many modern gas turbine engines, air is used to cool the turbine blades, in a similar manner to the nozzle guide vanes, which along with modern materials minimise "creep".

4.8 Free Turbines.

In this context the free turbine is mounted on a separate set of ball or roller bearings and is not connected to the compressor in any way. Its principle of operation is basically the same as the main or power turbines. The energy imparted into the free turbine may be used to drive a propeller, when it is more commonly known as a turboshaft engine, or as a free turbine which may be used to drive a helicopter rotor via the appropriate gear boxes.

Fig.4-10 shows an example helicopter gas turbine of the free turbine type.

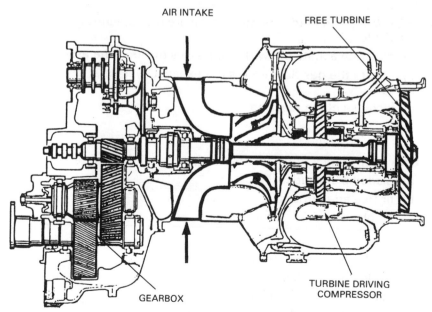

Fig.4-10. Free Turbine Engine.

TEST YOURSELF 4
TURBINES

1. Nozzle guide vanes:
   (a) tend to straighten the gas flow.
   (b) are fitted immediately after the turbine assembly.
   (c) give the gas a swirl.

   Ref. 4.2.

2. The nozzle guide vanes are normally:
   (a) divergent.
   (b) convergent.
   (c) concave.

   Ref. 4.2.

3. The gas temperature:
   (a) increases as it passes through the turbine.
   (b) remains constant as it passes through the turbine.
   (c) reduces as it passes through the turbine.

   Ref. 4.2.

4. The nozzles and blades of the turbine are manufactured with a state of twist to:
   (a) generate a state of swirl as it passes through the assembly.
   (b) ensure the gas flow enters the exhaust system at uniform axial velocity.
   (c) increase blade reaction.

   Ref. 4.2.

5. Loss of efficiency of turbine blade tips are minimised by:
   (a) blade tip shrouds.
   (b) fir tree attachments.
   (c) air bleed.

   Ref. 4.5.

6. Turbine blade "creep" may be reduced by:
   (a) blade tip shrouds.
   (b) material and air cooling.
   (c) creep restrainers.

   Ref. 4.7 & 4.4.

7. The main turbine/compressor engine shaft is normally mounted on:
    (a) needle roller bearings.
    (b) ball bearings only.
    (c) ball or roller bearings.

Ref. 4.4.

8. Modern gas turbine engine turbine blades are normally attached by:
    (a) the fir tree method.
    (b) the De Laval Bulb Root.
    (c) the BMW, Hollow Blade.

Ref. 4.4.

9. A free turbine is:
    (a) connected to the high pressure compressor of a two spool engine.
    (b) not connected to the compressor.
    (c) connected to the low pressure compressor.

Ref. 4.8.

10. As the gas flow passes through the turbine assembly the velocity of the gas flow will:
    (a) initially fall and then rise in the jet pipe.
    (b) remain relatively constant.
    (c) initially rise and then fall in the jet pipe.

Ref. 4.2.

4a

EXHAUST SYSTEM

4a.1 Introduction.

The exhaust system of the gas turbine engine passes the discharge gases to atmosphere. The gas leaves the turbine and on most subsonic aircraft, the gases are directed at high velocity, in a turbojet engine, and pressure to produce thrust. In a turbo-prop engine the exhaust gases are relatively low as most of the energy is absorbed in driving the turbines to drive the compressor and also the propeller.

The design of the exhaust system exerts a considerable influence on the performance of the engine. The areas of the jet pipe and propelling or outlet nozzle affect the turbine entry temperature, the mass airflow and the velocity and pressure of the exhaust jet.

The temperature of the exhaust gases entering the exhaust system is normally between 550 degrees C and 850 degrees C according to the type of engine. Turbo-prop and By-pass engines have a much cooler exhaust gas temperature. With the use of afterburning, or reheat, the temperatures in the jet pipe could be as high as 1500 degrees C or higher, however, due to the pattern of the flame and the system of cooling the impact of the higher temperature is not felt by the walls of the jet pipe. However, a higher temperature than normal will exist which dictates the use of materials and a form of construction which will resist cracking and distortion and also minimise the conduction of heat to the surrounding aircraft structure. The afterburner jet pipe also requires a variable exhaust, or propelling, nozzle. This may take the form of a simple two position nozzle or a true variable position nozzle which can be positioned at any point between fully closed and fully open. The purpose of such nozzles are to give the engine the capability of matching the different volumes of gas flow which occur when afterburning is on or off.

4a.2 The Basic Exhaust System.

Fig.4a-1 shows a basic exhaust system.

As the gas leaves the turbine it has a velocity in the order 750 to 1200 feet per second, however as velocities of this order produce high fiction losses the speed of flow is decreased by diffusion. The reduction in velocity is achieved by the use of a divergent duct formed between the exhaust pipe and the exhaust cone, or exhaust unit. This has the effect of maintaining a fairly constant gas stream pressure from the turbine to the exhaust outlet, temperature will fall very slightly in the exhaust pipe and velocity will decrease as it passes through the turbine and then slightly increase as it passes from the turbine to the exhaust outlet where depending on the outlet nozzle design, will accelerate.

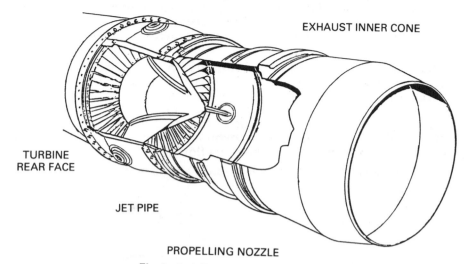

EXHAUST INNER CONE

TURBINE
REAR FACE

JET PIPE

PROPELLING NOZZLE

Fig.4a-1. A Basic Exhaust System.

The exhaust cone, just aft of the turbine outlet, prevents the exhaust gases from flowing across the rear face of the turbine disc. The velocity at the exhaust unit outlet is held to a velocity in the order of about Mach 0.5, that is approximately 950 feet per second. Losses also occur due to residual whirl velocity in the gas stream from the turbine, to reduce these effects, the support struts of the cone in the exhaust pipe are designed to straighten out the gas flow as it leaves the turbine.

The exhaust gases pass to atmosphere through the propelling nozzle which, in a basic exhaust system, normally forms a convergent duct, this will in turn cause the gas velocity to increase. In a turbojet engine the exit velocity of the exhaust gas is subsonic at low thrust conditions only. During most operating conditions the exit velocity reaches the speed of sound in relation to the exhaust gas temperature and the propelling nozzle is then said to be choked, that is no further increase in velocity can be obtained unless the temperature is increased. As the upstream total pressure is increased above the value at which the propelling nozzle choked, the static pressure of the gases at exit increase above atmospheric pressure. This pressure difference across the propelling nozzle gives what is known as pressure thrust and is effective over the nozzle exit area. This is additional thrust to that obtained due to the momentum change of the gas stream. It is important the propelling nozzle is of the correct size as it is designed to obtain the correct balance of pressure, temperature and thrust. With a small nozzle these values increase, however, there is a possibility of the engine surging, whilst with a large nozzle the values obtained are too low. On some engines variable nozzles are used to minimise such problems. The nozzle area is increased or decreased, to suit the conditions required. When this type of nozzle is used, an increase in flow area through the nozzle enables easier starting and reduces the risk of surge, this being primarily due to a reduction in the turbine back pressure. With a reduced nozzle area the maximum thrust is increased. The variation in the nozzle area also enables low specific fuel consumption to be attained during some part of the engine operating range.

The by-pass engine has two gas streams which are ejected through the jet pipe to atmosphere, the cool by-pass airflow and the hot turbine discharge gases. Although the by-pass airflow may be exhausted separately, on some engines it is the usual practice to mix the two flows before they leave the engine. This is done by a mixer unit which allows the by-pass air to flow into the exhaust gas flow in a manner which ensures a thorough mixing of the two flows.

Fig.4a-2 shows an example of a by-pass air mixer unit.

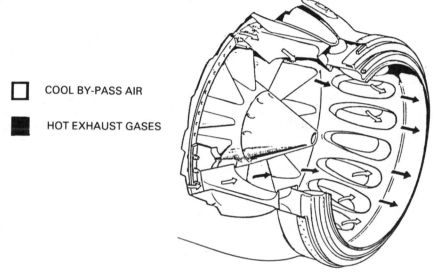

☐   COOL BY-PASS AIR

■   HOT EXHAUST GASES

Fig.4a-2. By-pass Air Mixer Unit.

4b

REHEAT/AFTERBURNING

4b.1 Introduction.

Reheat or afterburning is a method employed on some engines to augment the basic thrust of an engine to provide additional power for take off, and in some cases accelerate to cruise speed. Few civil aircraft use reheat or afterburning.

The alternative to the use of reheat would be to employ the use of a larger and more powerful engine which would result in increased weight, larger frontal area and fuel consumption. As such penalties are not always acceptable, reheat is a possible alternative.

Reheat or afterburning is a system primarily designed to augment thrust for short periods of time and consists of the introduction and burning of fuel between the turbine and the jet pipe propelling nozzle utilising the oxygen remaining in the exhaust gases to support combustion. The resultant increase in the temperature of the exhaust gas gives an increased velocity to the jet leaving the propelling nozzle and thus increases the engine thrust.

As the temperature of the reheat flame may be in excess of 1700 degrees C, the burners are normally located so that the flame is concentrated around the axis of the jet pipe, thereby allowing a proportion of the turbine discharge gas to flow along the wall of the jet pipe and therefore maintain the wall of the jet pipe at a safe temperature value.

Fig.4b-1 shows the location of an afterburner in a jet pipe assembly.

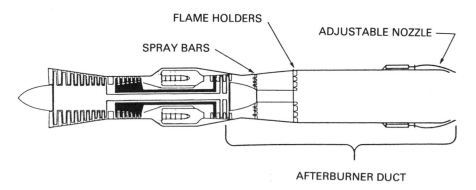

Fig.4b-1. Location of Afterburner Unit.

Normally the afterburning, or reheat, jet pipe assembly is larger than a conventional jet pipe would be for the same engine, this is done to achieve a reduced velocity gas stream. To provide for operations under all conditions, an afterburning jet pipe is fitted with either a two position propelling nozzle or a variable propelling nozzle. The nozzle is closed during non-afterburning operation. However, when afterburning is selected the nozzle opens to provide a suitable exit area for the increased gas stream. This prevents an excessive build up of back pressure which would affect the normal operation of the engine.

The thrust of an afterburning engine is slightly less, without afterburning operation, than that of a similar engine without afterburning, this is due to the restrictions caused to the gas flow by the afterburner equipment in the jet pipe. The overall weight of the engine is also increased due to the additional equipment and the larger and stronger jet pipe.

4b.2   Afterburner Operation.

The gas stream on leaving the turbine is in the order of a flow velocity of 750 to 1200 feet per second, however, as this velocity is far too high for a stable flame to be maintained, the flow is diffused before it enters the afterburner combustion zone, that is to say, the flow velocity is reduced and the pressure increases, however, it must be noted that the speed of burning of kerosine at normal mixture ratios is only a few feet per second, any fuel lit, even in the diffused gas stream will quickly be extinguished. To overcome this problem a form of flame stabiliser is fitted downstream of the fuel burners to provide a region in which turbulent eddies are formed to assist combustion, and where the local gas velocity is further reduced to a figure at which flame stabilisation occurs whilst combustion is in operation.

An atomised fuel spray is fed into the jet pipe through a number of burners. The burners are arranged to provide an even distribution of fuel over the whole flame area. Combustion is initiated by an igniter plug adjacent to the burner, or by a hot sheet of flame which originates in the engine combustion chamber, this latter method is known as hot shot ignition. Due to the increased temperature the gases expand and finally accelerate through the propelling nozzle to provide additional thrust.

4b.3   Thrust Increase with Afterburning.

The degree of the increase of thrust with afterburning depends solely upon the ratio of the absolute jet pipe temperatures before and after the extra fuel has been burnt. Some minor losses may be incurred, due mainly to restrictions created by the afterburning equipment in the jet pipe, and also gas flow momentum changes.

4b.4   Afterburning Control.

The afterburner/reheat system requires two basic functions to be controlled, the fuel flow and the propelling nozzle, it is important that these functions work perfectly in co-ordination with each other. When afterburning is selected on, automatically the propelling nozzle area increases, or opens, the degree the propelling nozzle opens will be dependent upon the degree of afterburning selected which in turn dictates the fuel flow to the afterburners. When the nozzle area is increased the fuel flow increases, and when the nozzle area is reduced the fuel flow reduces. The fuel flow sensing device ensures that the pressure ratio across the turbine remains unchanged and that the engine is unaffected by the operation of the afterburning, regardless of the nozzle aea and fuel flow.

Due to the large fuel flows required to supply the afterburner when it is in operation, an additional fuel pump is needed. This pump is normally of a centrifugal type and is energised automatically when the after-burning is selected.

4c

THRUST REVERSAL

4c.1   Introduction.

The progressive development of the modern airliner has seen a considerable increase in both aircraft weight and landing speed, as a result constant research has sought means of reducing the length of the landing run. A major contribution to reducing the landing run length is the fitting of thrust reversal to the gas turbine engine. Thrust reversal is normally only fitted to turbo-jet engines, and provides a simple method of slowing the aircraft down quickly by reversing the direction of the exhaust gases thus using engine power as a deceleration force. Use of this method of deceleration avoids overheating of wheel brakes, and makes landing on wet, or ice and snow covered, runways much safer. Some aircraft have been designed to use thrust reversal in flight to reduce aircraft speed, this, however, is not the normal modern practice.

Fig.4c-1 shows examples of the effects of use of thrust reversal against wheel brakes only.

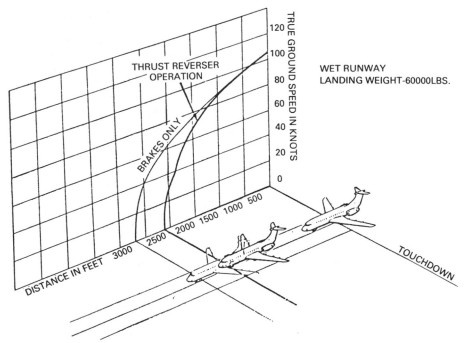

Fig.4c-1. Effects of Thrust Reversal Against Wheel Brakes Only.

4c.2 Turbo-Prop Aircraft.

On turbo-prop powered aircraft, thrust reversal is achieved by reversing the pitch of the propeller, this method is widely used and is discussed in depth in this series of books in the volume on propellers.

4c-3. Principle of Operation.

There are several methods employed to achieve the controlled reversal of thrust, generally the principle is the same, and it is only the mechanism used that tends to differ. Two methods are described in this chapter.

(a) Clamshell Door System.

Normally this type of arrangement is operated pneumatically, that is, compressed air is used to control the position of the doors. Normal engine operation is not affected by the system as the ducts through which the exhaust gases remain closed by the doors until reverse thrust is selected by the pilot.

On selection of reverse thrust the doors rotate to uncover the ducts and close the normal gas stream exit. Deflector vanes then direct the gas stream in a forward direction so that the jet thrust opposes the forward motion of the aircraft. Ideally the gas should be directed in a completely forward direction, however it is not possible to achieve this mainly due to aerodynamic reasons and a discharge angle of approximately 45 degrees is normally chosen. Reverse thrust power is normally about half the amount available for forward propulsion.

There are a number of safety features incorporated in the system. The pilot is prevented from selecting thrust reversal unless the engine is running at a lower power setting. On selection, the engine throttle cannot be opened to a high power setting if the doors fail to move into a full thrust reverse position. Should the operating pressure fall during thrust reversal, a mechanical lock holds the doors in the fully forward, or full thrust reversal, position. This lock cannot be released until the air pressure is restored.

Fig.4c-2 shows an example thrust reversal unit and Fig.4c-3 shows a more detailed example of the clamshell type.

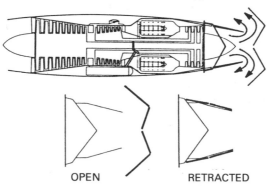

OPEN   RETRACTED

Fig.4c-2. Example Thrust Reversal Unit.

61

(b) Retractable Ejector System.
The retractable ejector system is normally both hydraulically and pneumatically operated and uses a bucket type door to reverse the jet stream.

On selection of reverse thrust, hydraulic pressure moves the ejector rearwards over the propelling nozzle, the buckets are then rotated by a pneumatic actuator to deflect the gas stream in a forward direction. A number of safety features are fitted to provide the same basic safety functions as those fitted to the clamshell door type.

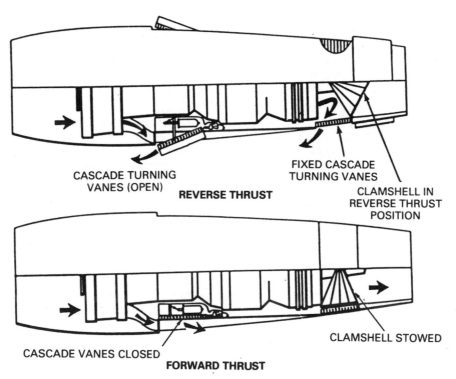

CASCADE TURNING
VANES (OPEN)   **REVERSE THRUST**

FIXED CASCADE
TURNING VANES

CLAMSHELL IN
REVERSE THRUST
POSITION

CASCADE VANES CLOSED
FORWARD THRUST

CLAMSHELL STOWED

Fig.4c-3. Clamshell Type Thrust Reverser.

TEST YOURSELF 4a, b & c

1. The support struts of the cone in an exhaust system:
   (a) are sometimes used to straighten out the exhaust gases.
   (b) give the exhaust gases a swirl effect.
   (c) are fitted always to support the cone only.

   Ref. 4a.2.

2. In a By-Pass engine, the by-pass exhaust is:
   (a) always exhausted separately.
   (b) always mixed with the normal exhaust gas in the jet pipe.
   (c) sometimes mixed with the normal exhaust gases in the jet pipe.

   Ref. 4a.2.

3. In an engine fitted with an afterburner, relative to an identical engine without an afterburner, under normal operation without reheat it:
   (a) will produce the same power.
   (b) will produce greater power.
   (c) will produce less power.

   Ref. 4b.1.

4. In a reheat system, with a variable position propelling nozzle, when reheat is selected:
   (a) the nozzle will remain in the same position.
   (b) the nozzle will open.
   (c) the nozzle will close.

   Ref. 4b.1.

5. In a clamshell door type thrust reversal system, when reverse is selected, the exhaust gases are:
   (a) discharged at approximately 45 degrees.
   (b) discharged at 90 degrees.
   (c) fully reversed.

   Ref. 4c.3.

5

FUEL SYSTEMS

5.1 Introduction.

The primary function of an aircraft gas turbine fuel system is to supply clean fuel, free from vapour, at the required pressure and flow rates to the engine under a wide variety of operating conditions. Generally speaking, the fuel system is designed to satisfy the requirements of the particular aircraft to which it is fitted.

5.2 Basic Fuel System.

The following is a basic fuel system to familiarise the reader with the essential components and their function within the fuel system.

(a) Fuel Tank.

The fuel tank is the primary component in which the fuel is stored within the airframe structure. The locations of the fuel tanks on larger aircraft are varied. Fig.5-1 shows some of the typical locations of the tanks of a large fuel system.

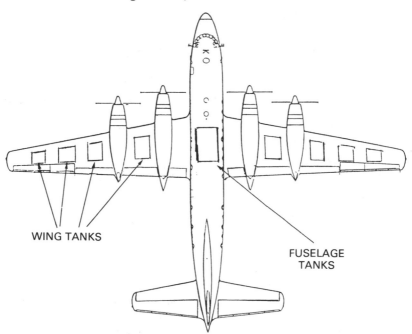

Fig.5-1. Fuel Tank Locations.

(b) Fuel Tank Types.

There are three basic types of fuel tank used on commercial aircraft.

   (i) Rigid.

This type of fuel tank is constructed from aluminium alloy, or similar light alloy, and takes the form of a rigid structure supported within a convenient space within the airframe. Fig.5-2 shows an example of a rigid fuel tank.

   (ii) Flexible Fuel Tanks.

This type of fuel tank is normally manufactured from synthetic rubber and is housed within a space in the airframe structure, normally of lightweight construction specifically shaped to receive the flexible tank. The flexible tank, sometimes called bag type tanks, may be manufactured in somewhat irregular shapes to make good use of every valuable space for fuel. Fig.5-2 shows an example flexible fuel tank.

   (iii) Integral Tanks.

The volume which forms the fuel tank is a part of the airframe structure which is sealed to make it fuel tight. This type of tank is widely used on modern aircraft as it makes full use of the space available and saves considerable weight. An example Integral Tank is shown in Fig.5-2.

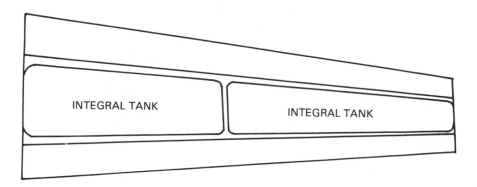

TANK AREA PART OF STRUCTURE BETWEEN MAIN AND REAR
SPARS. PARTS OF LEADING AND TRAILING EDGES MAY ALSO FORM
FUEL STORAGE TANKS

Fig.5-2. An Example Integral Tank.

(c) General.

The fuel tank incorporates:

   (i) A fuel contents sensor which through a transmitter indicates the fuel contents in the cockpit.

   (ii) A filter at the outlet from the tank and sometimes a filter is also fitted within the filler neck.

(iii) On many types a means of pressurising the tank, usually by bleed air, from the engine compressor, suitably cooled and pressure regulated. This is carried out to prevent the fuel bubbling at high altitude.

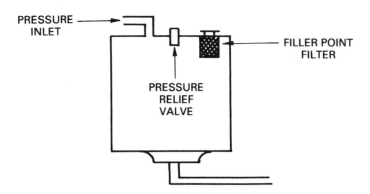

(d) Low Pressure Fuel Pump.

The low pressure fuel pump, usually called the "Booster Pump", is normally an electrically operated pump and is often connected to the underside of the fuel tank. It is controlled by an "On/Off" switch in the cockpit. Its primary purpose is to maintain a low pressure, normally at least atmospheric pressure, in the fuel system between the pump itself and the main or engine driven pump (High Pressure Pump) in order to prevent or minimise vapour locks occurring in the components and pipelines. The Booster Pump is also provided with a by-pass so that in the event of failure of the Booster Pump fuel can still be drawn through the Booster Pump by the engine driven pump to maintain a fuel supply to the engine. Adjacent to the Booster Pump selector switch is an indicator light which, when the pump is switched on the light illuminates until pressure has built up in the system to a specific value and then the light extinguishes.

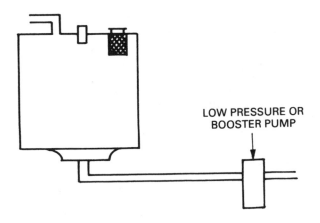

(e) Fuel ON/OFF Cock (Low Pressure Fuel Cock).

This is a simple Fuel ON, Fuel OFF Cock or valve, which may be operated from the cockpit electrically by an electric actuator, or mechanically by a lever mounted in the cockpit which is operated manually which operates the valve, remotely situated, by a mechanical linkage.

Some larger aircraft have an emergency mechanical system to operate the Low Pressuce Cock in the event the electrical system fails.

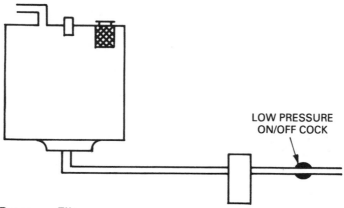

LOW PRESSURE
ON/OFF COCK

(f) Low Pressure Filter.

A filter is fitted in the low pressure fuel system to ensure a clean supply of fuel to the engine. The filter is normally fitted with a relief valve or by-pass valve so that in the event the filter element, that part of the assembly which removes dirt from the fuel, becomes blocked, or clogged, a supply of unfiltered fuel will continue to be pumped to the engine. Problems may arise in respect of filters in fuel systems due to ice particles forming in the fuel. Water can accumulate in suspension in the fuel and as the aircraft climbs to high altitude and the temperature reduces, the water in the fuel may form ice particles. Initially the filter element will prevent such ice particles passing further into the fuel system and fuel will continue to be supplied to the engine. Eventually, however, the ice will build up and block the element and also the relief or by-pass valve leading to fuel starvation of the engine. It should be noted that while the water content of the fuel is in liquid form it presents no serious danger to the engine, therefore if the water is prevented from forming into ice particles fuel starvation will be avoided. To achieve this the fuel is heated prior to the filter, therefore preventing the formation of ice in the fuel and therefore preventing the filter element becoming blocked by ice. The fuel may be heated by a number of methods, firstly it may be heated by bleed air from the high pressure zone of the compressor of the engine. Alternatively the fuel may be heated by a heat exchanger utilising the oil from the engine lubrication system as the heating medium and in this system the oil will be cooled at the same time. Temperature control is exercised in both systems to maintain a specific fuel temperature.

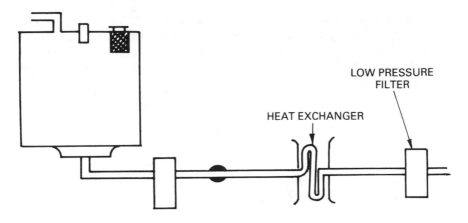

LOW PRESSURE
FILTER

HEAT EXCHANGER

(g) High Pressure Fuel Pump (Engine Driven Pump).
   The majority of engine driven pumps are of the swash plate type
   and are capable of maintaining a constant pressure and varying the
   volume of fuel they deliver according to the demands of the engine,
   in conjunction with the throttle setting and the automatic control
   systems. A Swash Plate Type Pump is shown in Fig.5-3.

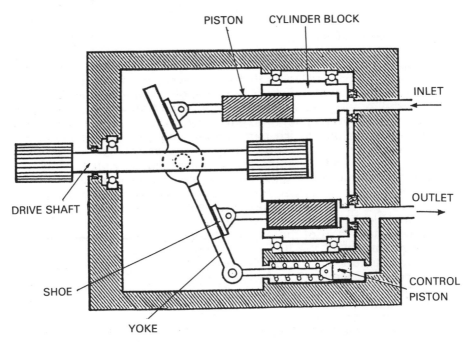

PISTON   CYLINDER BLOCK

INLET

OUTLET

DRIVE SHAFT

SHOE

CONTROL
PISTON

YOKE

Swash Plate Type Pump Principle of Operation,
Variable Volume Type.
This type of pump is similar in construction to the fixed volume
pump of the same basic type, but the cylinder block and drive shaft
are co-axial. The pistons are attached to shoes which rotate against

a stationary yoke, and the angle between the yoke and cylinder block is varied to increase or decrease pump stroke to suit system requirements. Fig.5-?? shows the operation of the pump. When pressure in the system is low, as would be the case when the throttle is opened, spring pressure on the control piston turns the yoke to its maximum angle, and the pistons are at full stroke, delivering maximum output to the system. When the actuator has completed its stroke, pressure builds up until the control piston moves the yoke to the minimum stroke piston; in this position a small flow through the pump is maintained, to lubricate the working parts, overcome internal leakage and dissipate heat. On some pumps a solenoid-operated depressurising valve is used to block delivery to the system, and to off-load the pump.

(h) Fuel Flow Control System.

In most modern gas turbine fuel systems the principle of a FLOW CONTROL SYSTEM is used, earlier engines operated with a pressure controlled fuel system. In the flow control system the fuel pump delivery pressure is sensitive to engine speed, therefore at low engine rpm the fuel pump delivery pressure is quite low. The flow control system is very compact and with the exception of the engine speed governor, all other devices are contained within one combined fuel control unit.

The High Pressure Fuel Pump delivery pressure is controlled by the Fuel Control Unit and the rpm of the High Pressure Fuel Pump is controlled by the Engine Speed Governor. The servo pressure in the pump which dictates the piston stroke and therefore the delivery of the pump is supplied by the Altitude Sensing Unit which is part of the Fuel Control Unit.

At any steady running condition below governed speed, the fuel pump delivery is controlled to a fixed value by the Altitude Sensing Unit. As the throttle is slowly opened the pressure in the pump servo piston supply increases, in turn the pump output increases. Any variation in engine air intake pressure, due to a change in aircraft forward speed or altitude, is sensed by a capsule in the Altitude Sensing Unit, this causes the unit to respond reducing the pump delivery in the event the intake pressure reduces, and the opposite will occur should the intake pressure increase.

During a rapid acceleration, the rapid movement of the throttle will cause an increased supply of fuel to the combustion chambers which will not be matched by an adequate supply of air from the compressor. The result of this unbalanced fuel/air ratio will be an increase in engine gas temperature and possibly compressor surge. It is essential therefore, to have an Acceleration Control Unit to give a corresponding lag in the rate of fuel flow increase.

The compoments in the fuel control system are very complex and this description is purely to give the reader a basic understanding of their purpose.

(i) High Pressure Fuel Cock (Fuel Shut-Off Cock).

The High Pressure Cock is essentially a sophisticated on/off cock. They may be operated manually, as on many older aircraft types, or they are operated automatically in conjunction with the throttle as part of the automatic start system of the engine. Normally the fuel is pressurised before the High Pressure Cock is opened, to ensure the fuel flows smoothly when it is opened there is a pressurising valve incorporated within the assembly. On engine shut down the High Pressure Cock is closed to starve the engine fuel manifold of fuel. On some modern fuel systems the High Pressure Cock control in the cockpit takes the form of a Circuit Breaker as opposed to a lever.

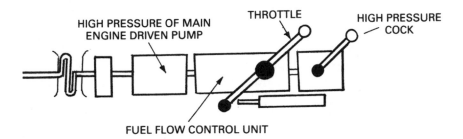

HIGH PRESSURE OF MAIN ENGINE DRIVEN PUMP — THROTTLE — HIGH PRESSURE COCK — FUEL FLOW CONTROL UNIT

5.3 Engine Fuel Manifold.

Fuel is supplied from the fuel supply system to the engine fuel manifold system. On most modern systems there are two manifolds: the main burner manifold and the primary burner manifold, both of which are explained in the section on combustion chambers.

5.4 Water Injection.

(a) Introduction.

As with a piston engine, the maximum power output of a gas turbine engine depends largely upon the density of the airflow passing through the engine. As altitude is increased the density of the atmosphere reduces and as a result power reduces. Equally power will be lost, or a reduction in thrust, will occur when the ambient air temperature increases. Under such conditions power output may be restored, or in some cases, boosted for take off by cooling the airflow with water or water/methanol. Firstly if methanol is added to the water it gives anti-freeze properties, and also provides an additional source of fuel.

(b) Injection.

There are two basic methods of introducing the cooland (water/methanol) into the engine airflow.

    (i)   The coolant on some engines is sprayed directly into the intake, or compressor inlet. When the injection system is switched on, water/methanol is pumped from a tank mounted in the airframe to a control unit. The control unit meters the flow of mixture to the compressor inlet through a metering valve which is operated by a servo piston. Engine oil is used as the medium to operate the servo system and a servo valve controls the supply of engine oil. The degree of servo valve opening is set by a control system which is sensitive to the propeller shaft torque, on turboprops, oil pressure, and to atmospheric pressure acting on a capsule within the control unit assembly. Inlet injection systems are normally used on centrifugal compressor engines.

(ii) The alternative method of water/methanol injection is the combustion chamber injection system which is more suitable to axial flow compressor engines. On selecting water/methanol injection, the coolant flows from the tank, in the airframe, to an air driven turbine pump which delivers it to the water flow sensing unit. The water, or water/methanol, flows from the sensing unit down each burner feed arm and is sprayed from jets onto the flame tube swirl vanes, thus cooling the air passing into the chamber combustion zone. The coolant pressure between the sensing unit and the discharge jets is sensed by the fuel control system, which automatically resets the engine speed governor to give a higher maximum engine speed as would be required for boosted power for certain take off conditions such as take off in high temperature situations.

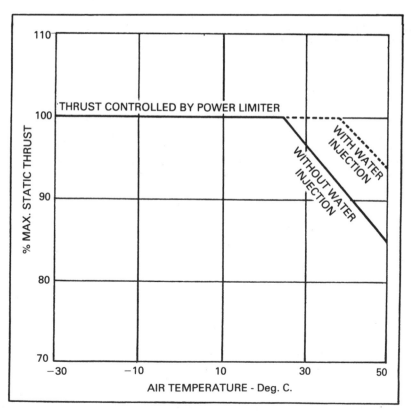

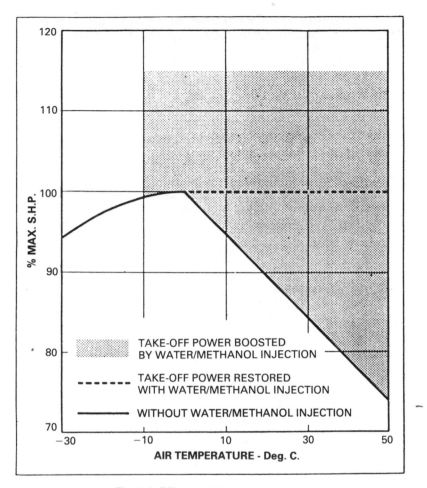

Fig.5-4. Effects of Coolant Injection.

The water flow sensing unit only opens when the correct pressure difference is obtained between compressor air delivery pressure and water pressure. The system is brought into operation when the engine throttle lever is moved to take off position, causing microswitches to operate and select the air for the turbine pump. The sensing unit also forms a non-return valve to prevent air pressure feeding back from the discharge jets, and also provision is made for an indicator light to illuminate when water, or water/methanol is flowing.

Fig.5-4 shows the effects of coolant injection in a turbojet engine and a turboprop engine.

TEST YOURSELF 5
FUEL SYSTEMS

1. The low pressure fuel pump:
   (a) is normally driven mechanically by the engine.
   — (b) is normally electrically driven.
   (c) is driven hydraulically by the engine lubrication system.
   Ref. 5.2.

2. The low pressure filter is prevented from being blocked by ice particles in the fuel by:
   (a) a by-pass valve being fitted to the filter.
   — (b) pre heating the fuel.
   (c) an ice guard mounted prior to the filter.
   Ref. 5.2.

3. The high pressure fuel pump is normally driven:
   — (a) mechanically by the engine.
   (b) hydraulically.
   (c) electrically by the engine.
   Ref. 5.2.

4. The high pressure fuel cock:
   (a) controls fuel flow from the tank to the fuel flow control unit.
   — (b) is used to control fuel flow to the engine.
   (c) is used to pressurise the fuel tank.
   Ref. 5.2.

5. Fuel is fed to the engine from the supply system via:
   — (a) the fuel manifold.
   (b) the fuel injection jets.
   (c) the injector control unit.
   Ref. 5.2.

6

ENGINE STARTING SYSTEMS

6.1 Introduction.

To successfully start the gas turbine engine two systems are required, the ignition system and the fuel system, both discussed in depth in chapter three.

The fuel system provides atomised fuel to the burners located in the combustion chambers, and the ignition system supplies a spark to ignite the fuel air mixture on start up. Ignition is also provided at other times and these will be discussed later in this chapter.

In order to achieve the correct air/fuel ratio, in the order of 15:1 to 18:1 a flow of air must be supplied to the combustion chambers, and this is normally achieved by rotating the compressor at sufficient rpm to produce an adequate airflow.

During engine starting the two systems, fuel and ignition, must operate simultaneously which is co-ordinated and controlled automatically, after initiation of the start cycle, by an electrical circuit.

It is important to note at this stage the ideal theoretical air/fuel ratio is in the order of 15:1, however for practical purposes an air/fuel ratio in the order of 18/1 is more desirable producing a combustion temperature of approximately 1600 to 1800 degrees centigrade.

6.2 Start Sequence.

The start sequence is automatically co-ordinated and controlled on most modern systems, and a typical sequence is as follows:

(a) Start Selected.
   The selection of engine start will initiate the operation of the system that will rotate the compressor in order to create the desired airflow to successfully sustain engine operation. The methods used to rotate the engine in order to complete the start cycle are many and varied. The details of such systems will be discussed later in the chapter.

   The most common methods used to initiate the rotation of the engine are the use of an electrically operated starting motor and an air start system.

(b) As the start button is depressed, with electrical power "on" the starter motor or system rotates the engine, and at the same time ignition is also switched "on".

(c) After a pre-set time delay, which will normally correspond to a given build up of engine rpm, the HP Cock will move to the fuel on position and fuel is admitted to the combustion chambers.

Note: Some systems require the HP Cock to be moved to the on position manually as the required engine rpm are reached.

(d) Normally between 5 to 10 seconds after start sequence is initiated, light up occurs at which time the engine should have reached some 20 per cent of the maximum engine rpm.

(e) If combustion is successful the engine should reach self sustaining speed at 35 per cent of maximum engine rpm after a period of some 15 to 20 seconds after the commencement of the start sequence.

(f) The starter electrical circuit will normally cancel shortly after self sustaining speed.

(g) Idle rpm will be reached (some 55 to 60 per cent engine rpm), at approximately 30 seconds after the start button has been depressed.

Note: The figures stated above are just a guide.

6.3 Methods of Engine Starting.

As previously stated, the most common methods employed to rotate the engine to produce the required airflow for starting purposes are the electrical starting system and the air start system.

(a) Electrical Start System.
This system employs an electric motor coupled to the engine via a reduction gear mechanism and a ratchet or clutch assembly. The electric motor is normally DC and through the ratchet or clutch mechanism automatically disengages after the engine has started.

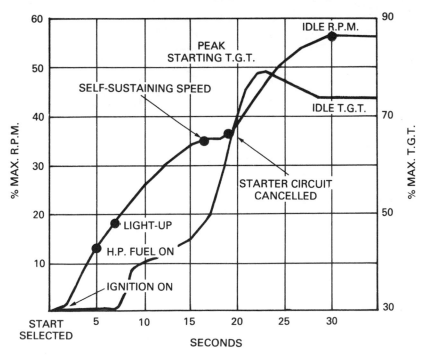

START SEQUENCE

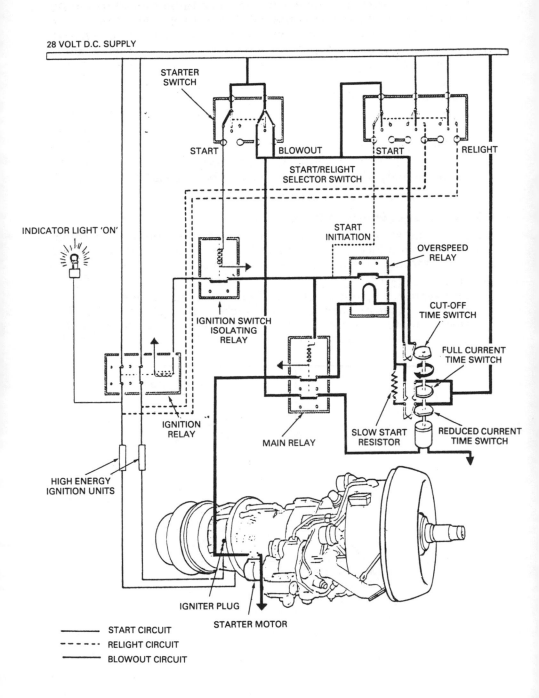

Fig.6-1. Low Voltage Start Circuit.

Depending on the system adopted, the electrical supply may be of a low or high voltage and is passed through a circuit of relays and resistances which permits the full voltage to be progressively increased as the starter gains speed and provides the power for the ignition system. The electrical supply is automatically cancelled when the starter load is reduced when the engine has successfully started or when the time cycle is completed.

Fig.6-1 shows an example electrical start system.

(b) Air Starting System.
Air starting is used on many modern civil aircraft for the starting of the gas turbine engines. Its primary advantages are, it is simple, economical to use, and comparatively light in weight. The air start type system has a turbine motor which is coupled to, via a clutch or ratchet assembly, the engine.

The starter turbine is supplied with air from a ground external source or from the auxiliary power unit, the air is fed to the turbine of the air starter motor causing it to rotate which then in turn rotates the gas turbine engine. Like the electrical start system, the air start system is automatically controlled once the start sequence has been initiated. An electrically operated air control valve is opened when engine start is selected and is automatically closed at a predetermined starter speed. The clutch also automatically disengages as the engine accelerates up to idling rpm and rotation of the starter ceases.

Fig.6-2 shows an example air start system.

Note: In a twin spooled compressor engine, on starting, the high pressure compressor is started by the starter motor and the airflow created rotates the low pressure compressor. The high pressure compressor is started first to reduce the tendency of surge.

6.4 Ignition.

As has been previously stated in para 6.2 initiation of ignition is an automatic function once the start sequence has been selected, and is also cancelled automatically. However, ignition is not only used during the start sequence it may also be used during take-off, relighting the engine after a "flame out" has occurred, and continuous operation in adverse weather conditions.

(a) Relighting.
As can be seen on the system shown in Fig.6-1 provision is made for relighting the engine in the event of a flame-out.

(b) On many aircraft provision is also made to sustain the operation of the ignition units during take-off or during flight in adverse weather conditions. In particular, during take off, should a flame-out occur due to compressor surge or stall, the igniters may immediately relight, or re-ignite the air/fuel mixture and avoid a much more serious situation developing. Ignition is also switched on during flights through heavy tropical storms where again there is an increased risk of flame-out.

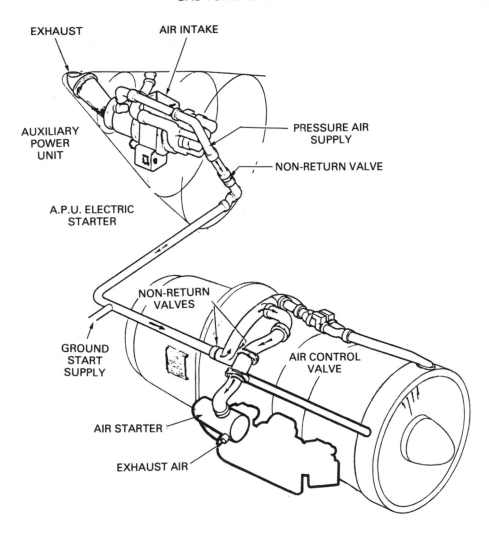

EXHAUST AIR INTAKE

AUXILIARY POWER UNIT

PRESSURE AIR SUPPLY

NON-RETURN VALVE

A.P.U. ELECTRIC STARTER

NON-RETURN VALVES

GROUND START SUPPLY

AIR CONTROL VALVE

AIR STARTER

EXHAUST AIR

Fig.6-2. Air Starter System.

6.5 Relighting.

If a flame-out occurs in flight the airflow passing through the engine will maintain a degree of rotation of the compressor and turbine assembly. To relight the engine all that is required is the operation of the ignition assuming an adequate fuel supply is available. Operation of the complete start sequence is not required, as the engine is still rotating (windmilling). A separate switch is provided in the ignition system to permit the start sequence to be by-passed and ignition only provided, this is termed the relight switch. The ability of the engine to successfully relight varies with forward speed and altitude of the aircraft. Details relating to relight procedures are given in Engine Performance and Handling.

TEST YOURSELF 6
ENGINE STARTING SYSTEMS

1. In an automatic electrical starting system the:
   - (a) ignition commences ten seconds after the start button has been pushed.
   - (b) ignition commences at the same time the starter motor engages.
   - (c) ignition commences when fuel starts flowing into the combustion system.

   Ref. 6.2.

2. In an electrically operated gas turbine start system, the electric motor:
   - (a) must be manually disconnected when the engine has reached the required rpm.
   - (b) is automatically switched off when the required rpm are reached.
   - (c) is automatically switched off after a specified period of time or the engine is at sustaining rpm.

   Ref. 6.3.

3. When relighting the engine due to a flame-out:
   - (a) the full start sequence must be used.
   - (b) the full start sequence may be by-passed and use of the relight button is made.
   - (c) auto ignition must be selected.

   Ref. 6.5.

4. In an air start system:
   - (a) air is blown through the compressor inlet to rotate the engine.
   - (b) air is blown through the turbine to rotate the engine.
   - (c) air is supplied to an air starter motor.

   Ref. 6.3.

5. On a twin spooled compressor engine, on starting:
   - (a) both compressor elements are rotated by the starter motor.
   - (b) the low pressure compressor is started by the motor.
   - (c) the high pressure compressor is started by the motor.

   Ref. 6.3.

7

LUBRICATION SYSTEMS

7.1 Introduction.

The primary function of the gas turbine engine lubrication system is to supply lubricating oil to the main bearings of the main drive shaft in order to provide adequate lubrication and also to cool the bearings. Fig.7-1 shows the location of the main bearings in a typical gas turbine engine. The number of main bearings vary depending on engine type, generally there are at least four or five main bearings which are normally of a ball or roller type. As well as lubricating the main bearings lubricating oil is also fed to ancillary drive gearboxes which drive such components as generators, hydraulic pumps and many other such items. In the case of a Turboprop Engine, the lubrication system also provides oil to the reduction gearing of the propeller drive mechanism.

The majority of gas turbine engine lubrication systems are of a self contained recirculatory type, that is a system with its own storage tank from which a pump draws the lubricating oil circulates it round the system, lubricating and cooling the bearings, gears, drives and other components, and then returns the oil to the tank.

7.2 Recirculatory Lubrication System.

(a) Tank.

The recirculatory type system first requires a storage tank which holds a reserve of oil to compensate for minor leakage, expansion of the oil due to temperature increase, and allows a space above the oil in the tank for frothing.

The tank usually incorporates a filter in the filler neck to prevent any foreign objects entering the tank and contaminating the oil. Some tanks also have an additional filter at the outlet from the tank.

Fig.7-2 shows an example oil tank.

(b) Oil Pump.

The pump is normally a fixed, or constant volume pump, delivering the same flow rate at constant engine rpm. The pump is driven by the engine and therefore its rpm, and of course its output, is directly related to engine rpm. The pressure in the system is not controlled by the pump, but by a Pressure Relief Valve situated after the pump.

The majority of modern gas turbine lubrication systems are fitted with more than one pump and they usually fall into two main types. There are normally two pressure pumps which supply the oil to the areas of the engine to be lubricated and a number of scavenge

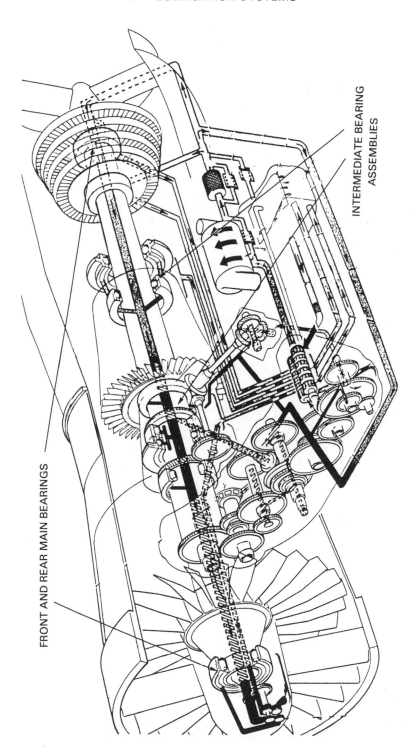

INTERMEDIATE BEARING ASSEMBLIES

FRONT AND REAR MAIN BEARINGS

Fig.7-1. Location of Main Bearings.

pumps which ensure the return oil is sucked from the bearings and other components and returned to the oil tank and main pressure pumps.

Fig.7-3 shows an example pump.

(c) Strainers.

In each return line a strainer is fitted to remove any particles of dirt, metal, or any other form of contamination to prevent their continuous recirculation and subsequent damage they may impart on the system and its components.

(d) Bearing Oil Seals.

The main bearings, usually of a ball or roller type, are subjected to very high temperatures, as a result the housings of the bearings and the bearings themselves are primarily cooled by the lubricating oil. Even after the cooling effects of the oil the temperatures remain very high, far too high to be sealed by conventional rubber or nylon type seals. The oil is pumped through the bearing housings under pressure and as such must be sealed to prevent the oil leaking out into the other areas of the engine. The seals take the form of a combined groove or thread shape backed up by air pressure to prevent the oil leaking out of its housing. Fig.7-4 shows some examples of air controlled seals.

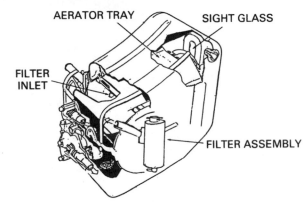

Fig.7-2. Oil Tank.

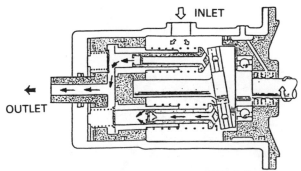

Fig.7-3. Fixed Volume Oil Pump.
Pressure is controlled by a Pressure Relief Valve.

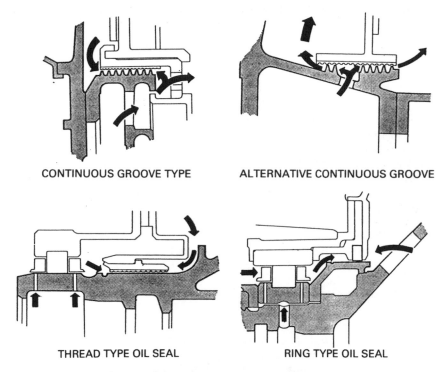

CONTINUOUS GROOVE TYPE   ALTERNATIVE CONTINUOUS GROOVE

THREAD TYPE OIL SEAL   RING TYPE OIL SEAL

Fig.7-4. Examples of Air Control Oil Seals.

(e) Magnetic Chip Detectors.

At strategic points in the system are located magnetic chip detectors. These are small plugs which are magnetic and attract ferrite based metal particles which may be in the lubricating oil. By examination of the chip detector and careful examination of any particles on it, the system can be health monitored. For example, certain types of particle may indicate the pump bearings are beginning to wear excessively.

Fig.7-5 shows an example installation of chip detectors.

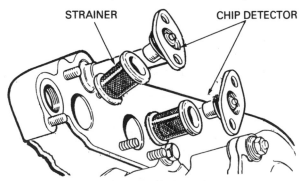

Fig.7-5. Example Chip Detector.

7.3 Expendable Lubrication System.

The expendable, or total loss lubricating system, is included in this book for comparison purposes. Generally this type of system was used on older types of engine and is only seen on older operational machines. Also the use of this type of system tended to be confined to small engines. The system is light in weight, as it requires no oil cooler, scavenge pumps or filters, and therefore is very simple in design.

The expendable lubricating system consists primarily of:

(a) Oil Supply.
    This may be achieved by one of two methods, either by an oil pump or by pressurising the oil tank. In the case of the pressurised oil tank method, this is automatically selected by the operation of the high pressure fuel cock during the engine start sequence.

(b) Oil Tank.
    It must be remembered, once the oil has been used for lubricating the engine bearings it is then dumped overboard, and no attempt is made to recirculate the oil. As a result the oil tank must be large enough to hold sufficient oil for the duration of the flight. Generally the flight duration of such engines is comparatively short. A typical consumption rate of oil for such an engine type would be 1.2 litres per hour.

(c) Oil Metering Valve.
    An oil metering valve is fitted to ensure a balanced supply of oil to the front bearing with the supply to the centre bearing. The rear bearing is normally supplied with oil that has been used to lubricate the front and main, or centre, bearing. After lubricating the rear bearing the oil is then ejected into the engine gas flow from the exhaust.

    Fig.7-6 shows an example of an expendable lubrication system.

7.4 Lubricating Oils.

Generally gas turbine engines use a low viscosity (thin) lubricating oil which is normally synthetic based and does not originate from mineral based crude oil.

Gas turbine lubricating oils must retain their lubricating properties and be resistant to oxidation at high temperatures. There are many types of synthetic oils used for gas turbine engines which are manufactured to rigid specifications, only those recommended for a particular engine must be used.

The gas turbine engine is able to use low viscosity oils due mainly to the absence of reciprocating components and heavy gear loading. The power requirement is therefore considerably reduced and starting the engine is less of a problem, particularly at low temperatures. Normal engine starts can be achieved with gas turbines at temperatures as low as −40 degrees C.

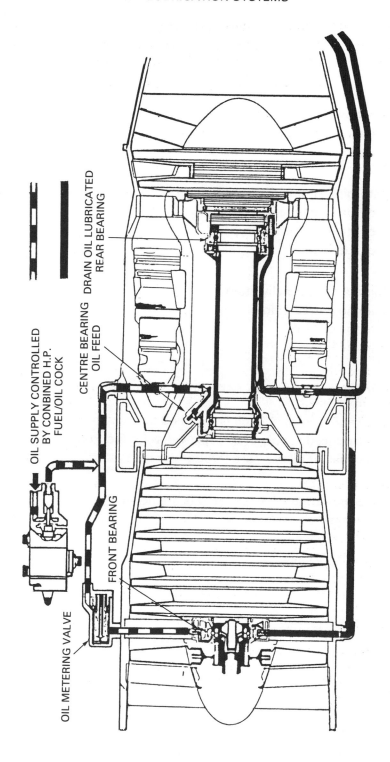

OIL SUPPLY CONTROLLED BY CONBINED H.P. FUEL/OIL COCK

CENTRE BEARING OIL FEED

DRAIN OIL LUBRICATED REAR BEARING

FRONT BEARING

OIL METERING VALVE

Fig.7-6. Expendable Lubrication System.

TEST YOURSELF 7
LUBRICATIONS SYSTEMS

1. The output of the engine driven oil pump:
  - (a) varies with engine rpm.
  - (b) remains constant at all engine rpm values.
  - (c) varies with engine demand.

Ref. 7.2.

2. Gas turbine engine main bearing oil seals are normally:
  - (a) of the synthetic rubber type.
  - (b) of the air controlled type.
  - (c) of a nylon type.

Ref. 7.2.

3. Strainers are normally fitted:
  - (a) in the pressure line.
  - (b) in the oil tank.
  - (c) in the return line.

Ref. 7.2.

4. Oil metering valves are normally fitted to the engine lubrication system to ensure:
  - (a) an equal amount of oil is supplied to each bearing.
  - (b) a balanced supply of oil is provided for the front bearing.
  - (c) a constant oil pressure throughout the system.

Ref. 7.3.

5. Gas turbine engine lubricating oils are normally:
  - (a) mineral based.
  - (b) natural based.
  - (c) synthetic based.

8

FIRE PROTECTION

8.1 Introduction.

Gas turbine installations and their associated equipment are designed and installed to minimise the occurrence of an engine fire. It is essential however that if a failure does occur that provision is made to detect and rapidly extinguish any such fire, and where possible, through the construction of the aircraft airframe, coupled with the extinguishing systems, fire is also prevented from spreading.

8.2 Fire Prevention.

The following features are some of the practices adopted by most engine and aircraft manufacturers to reduce the risk of fire and to prevent the spreading of a fire should it occur.

During the design and manufacture of the engine great effort is applied to ensure that all potential sources of flammable liquids and fluids are isolated from the "Hot End" of the engine.

External fuel and oil system pipelines and components are usually located around the compressor casings and separated from the combustion and turbine areas of the engine by fireproof bulkheads or heat shields. The area around the jet pipe, or exhaust, are constructed in a similar manner. Such areas, or zones, are usually ventilated to prevent the accumulation of fuel vapours which may present a fire risk.

All pipelines which carry fuel, lubricating oils, and hydraulic fluids are made fire resistant, and all electrical wiring, components and connections are made "flameproof", that is to say, they are incapable of igniting an inflammable vapour due to internal sparking. Sparking due to discharges of static electricity is prevented by "Bonding", that is all electrical and other components are connected to each other to provide continuity and therefore prevent the build up of static electricity in one location which could ultimately result in a sudden discharge large enough to ignite fuel vapours or other combustible materials. The method most commonly used to bond components together is via bonding leads.

The engine bays and cowlings are manufactured with adequate drainage to remove all inflammable fuels or fluids both in flight or on the ground, such drainage systems drain potential hazardous fuel or other liquid substances overboard.

To further reduce the build up of vapours in the engine bays or pods, air is sometimes bled from the boundary layer and ducted through the engine bay and then out to atmosphere. Usually such air bleed systems can be controlled by the pilot when they would be shut off if a fire extinguisher is fired, or selected, otherwise the extinguishant would be removed from the engine bay by the airflow stopping if fulfilling its function of smothering the fire.

8.3   Fire Detection.

It is essential that should a fire occur that it is detected rapidly in order the fire can be extinguished before it becomes too large. It is also important the detection system is reliable and will not give false fire warnings due to short circuiting which may result from vibration, chafing or the presence of moisture.

The fire detection system may comprise of one or two main types, the continuous element type or it may consist of a number of individually located detector units. In principle the presence of a fire is signalled by a change in the electrical impedance or the output voltage of the detector circuit. Remember, temperature increase in electrical terms results in a reduction in resistance. The variation of resistance or voltage will depend on the type of system used. The change of temperature, caused by the fire will create a signal which through an amplifier operates the warning indicator. Fire indication is normally through a light and/or an audible warning such as a bell, and the warning is cancelled only when the temperature returns to normal.

Test buttons or switches are normally provided to test the detection warning light circuits prior to flight.

Fig.8-1 shows an example installation of a detector system.

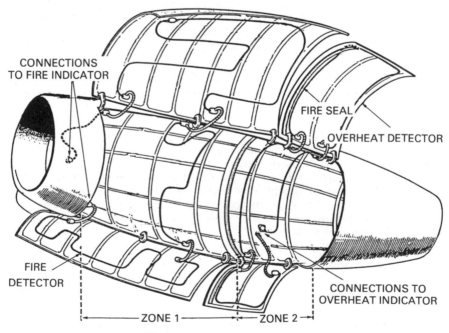

CONNECTIONS
TO FIRE INDICATOR

FIRE SEAL

OVERHEAT DETECTOR

FIRE
DETECTOR

CONNECTIONS TO
OVERHEAT INDICATOR

ZONE 1 ——— ZONE 2

Fig.8-1. Fire Detector System.

8.4 Fire Containment.

In the event a fire occurs in an aircraft engine, or in its respective bay or pod, it is vital to contain that fire in that area and prevent it from spreading to other parts of the aircraft. The cowlings which surround the engine are normally manufactured from light alloy which would be unable to contain the fire when the aircraft is static on the ground. In flight however, the airflow around the cowlings provides sufficient cooling to render them fireproof. Bulkheads which are designed to contain a fire, normally termed "fireproof bulkheads" or "firewalls" and do not have the benefit of airflow over them in flight, are usually manufactured from steel or titanium.

8.5 Fire Extinguishing System.

Normally in the event a fire is detected, in particular on multi engined aircraft, it is usual to immediately shut down the engine. Assume the cause of the fire is a fuel leak, allowing the engine to continue running simply means, the fire will continue to be fed by the engine's fuel system. In shutting the engine down the high pressure fuel cock to the affected engine will be closed starving the engine of further fuel. It is also essential to isolate the fuel system related to the engine which is affected by fire, this is done by closing the low pressure fuel cock, any fuel pumps or other components within the isolated area of fuel supply should be switched off.

The fire extinguishant used most commonly for gas turbine engines is methyl-bromide or one of the freon compounds. The fire extinguished is normally cylindrical in shape and is pressurised. Such extinguishers are termed "Fixed Fire Extinguishers", that is to say they are not portable as may be found clipped to the cockpit or cabin wall. Methyl-bromide extinguishers are normally coloured grey or blue.

The extinguisher is located outside the fire zone for which it is intended, normally such extinguishers would be located in the wing or an area of the airframe fairly close to its fire zone.

The methyl-bromide extinguisher is operated electrically by a push button or switch in the cockpit, as the button is depressed a small cartridge in the valve assembly attached to the extinguisher is fired releasing the extinguishant, directing it through a pipe or tube to the fire zone. In the fire zone the extinguishant is fed through tubes with a number of holes in them, designed to create a spray of extinguishant over a specific area of the engine or engine bay. The spray is highly concentrated and will normally last for a period of 0.5 to 2.0 seconds. The system may be designed with a single fire extinguisher and is generally termed a "Single Shot" system. Some systems are called "Two Shot Systems" where two extinguishers are employed with a selector switch which will give two shots at the suspected or indicated fire.

Fig.8-2 shows an example of the installed system incorporating a two shot capability.

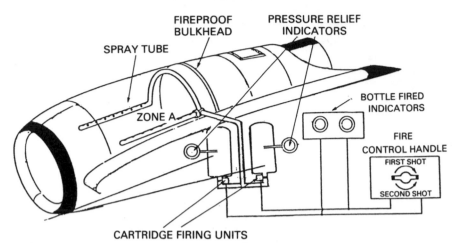

Fig.8-2. Two Shot Fire Extinguisher System.

Certain safety devices are fitted to the system. Firstly a relief valve is situated in the valve assembly so that in the event an extinguisher overpressurises, due to excess temperature. The relief valve opens allowing the extinguishant to escape to atmosphere rather than have an extinguisher explode and damage the aircraft structure. A small tube carries the extinguishant from the relief valve to a convenient port and then to atmosphere. In the end of the port is installed a small disc or diaphragm which may be coloured red or green. The extinguishant will burst the disc on escaping to atmosphere, this therefore provides the pilot with a quick external check, that if the disc is burst the extinguisher has overpressurised and discharged.

Fig.8-3 shows a methyl-bromide extinguisher and its related valve assembly.

8.6 Extinguisher.

Extinguishers vary in construction but are normally comprised of two main components (i) the steel or copper container and (ii) the discharge or operating head. A sectioned view of an extinguisher widely used in a two-shot system is shown in Fig.8-3. The container is in the form of a steel cylinder and has an externally threaded neck to which the discharge head is screwed and soldered. The discharge head contains two annular machined diaphragms, each bearing an externally-threaded spigot on which a hollow plug is screwed to form an annulus between its inner end and its respective diaphragm. Each annulus is connected by a 'flash' hole to a port containing the appropriate cartridge unit. Below, and concentric with each diaphragm and charge plug, is a radially adjustable light-alloy hollow junction box fitted with a union to which an extinguisher discharge pipe is connected. The lower end of the junction box is closed by a cap which embodies a discharge indicator pin.

A banjo coupling is fitted in the main body of the operating head and serves as a connection for a pressure discharge indicator.

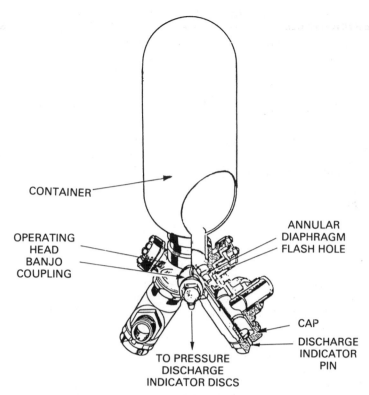

Fig.8-3. Methyl Bromide Extinguisher.

When either of the cartridge units are fired, sufficient pressure is created in the adjacent annulus to rupture the associated diaphragm. The spigot and charge plug assembly is thereby detached and forced down the hollow junction box beyond the outlet union and discharge pipe through which the extinguishant then flows to the spray pipes, rings, and/or manifolds. See Fig.8-3

8.7 Directional Flow Valves.

These valves are a special form of non-return valve designed for use in two-shot systems to allow the contents of one or several extinguishers to be directed into any one power plant. The methods of connection may vary between different aircraft systems, but the one shown in Fig.8-2 is typical and also serves to illustrate the two-shot operating sequence generally adopted. The extinguishers are controlled by individual firing switches each having three positions; No. 1, OFF and No. 2. When the port extinguisher switch is selected to the No. 1 position, the relevant cartridge unit in the port extinguisher is fired and the extinguisher is discharged to the port power plant. If the fire has not been extinguished, selection of the No. 2 position then causes the starboard extinguisher to be discharged also into the port power plant via the crossfeed line and port directional flow valve, the latter preventing extinguishant from entering the empty extinguisher of the port system. In order to extinguish a fire in the starboard engine, the starboard extinguisher switch is selected to its No. 1 position, and the relevant cartridge unit is fired so that extinguishant is discharged to the starboard power plant. If selection of the No. 2 position of the starboard extinguisher switch becomes necessary, then the port extinguisher will also be discharged into the starboard power plant via the appropriate crossfeed line and the starboard directional flow valve, which prevents charging the empty starboard extinguisher.

Note: In some types of aircraft, the cross connecting of selected extinguishers between engines is accomplished by means of transfer switches which are additional to the normal firing switches.

TEST YOURSELF 8
FIRE PROTECTION

1. The majority of fixed aircraft fire extinguisher systems use:
   - (a) Methly-bromide extinguishant.
   - (b) CO_2 extinguishant.
   - (c) Carbon Tetra Flouride extinguishant.

   Ref. 8.5.

2. The extinguisher in a fixed fire extinguisher system is activated:
   - (a) manually by a mechanical valve.
   - (b) electrically.
   - (c) by CO_2 gas pressure.

   Ref. 8.5.

3. A burst red disc at the atmospheric outlet of a fixed fire extinguisher system indicates:
   - (a) the system has been used to extinguish a fire.
   - (b) the system is unserviceable.
   - (c) the extinguisher has overpressurised.

   Ref. 8.5.

4. In flight, engine cowlings are fireproofed by:
   - (a) the airflow.
   - (b) titanium.
   - (c) asbestos lagging.

   Ref. 8.2.

5. Fire from electrical components due to static electricity build up is minimised by:
   - (a) ventilation.
   - (b) bonding.
   - (c) boundary air cooling.

   Ref. 8.2.

9

ICE PROTECTION SYSTEMS

9.1 Introduction.

Icing of gas turbine engines may occur during flight when flying through clouds containing supercooled water droplets and during ground operations in conditions of poor visibility with an air temperature near freezing.

The gas turbine engine requires protection against the formation and build up of ice in front of the engine in the intake region, and the leading edge of air intake ducts.

Fig.9-1 shows the areas of the engine and its intake which are equipped with ice protection devices.

9.2 Types of Ice Protection Employed on Gas Turbine Engines.

There are essentially two main types of ice protection system currently in use.

(a) Hot Air System.

(b) Electrical Systems.

9.3 Hot Air System.

The hot air system is widely used on turbojet engines and works on the principle of ducting hot air, normally bled from the high pressure region of the engine's compressor, which is then used to heat the skin surfaces at the engine intake and the leading edge of the engine inlet.

Fig.9-2 shows a hot air system and its components.

9.4 Hot Air System Operation.

Hot air is bled from the high pressure stages of the compressor, often the last stage, and is then ducted via a pressure regulating valve, which controls the pressure within the system. The air flow passes through light alloy ducting to the surfaces requiring protection, and is capable of maintaining the surface skin temperature above 0 degrees C. After the air has circulated through the system it is then discharged back into the compressor inlet or is just dumped overboard.

The pressure regulator valves are normally electrically actuated by either manual or automatic selection. The valves prevent excessive pressures being developed in the system and also limit the amount of air taken from the compressor therefore preventing excessive loss of performance particularly at higher engine speeds.

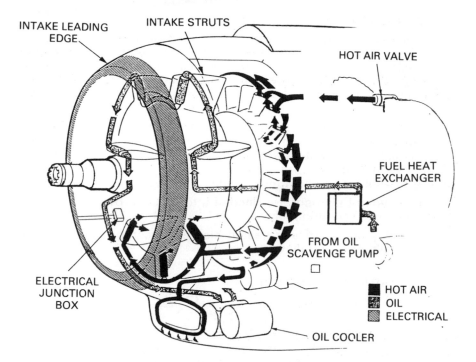

Fig.9-1. Ice Protection Devices.

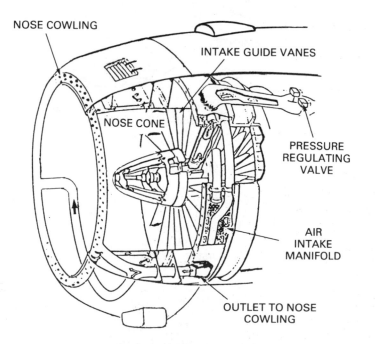

Fig.9-2. Hot Air De-icing.

9.5 Electrical System.

Electrical systems are more commonly used on turbo-prop engines primarily as this form of ice protection is best suited for the protection of propellers against ice formation. Electrically heated pad assemblies are bonded to air intake cowlings, the propeller blades and spinner, where applicable, and on some installations the oil cooler intake cowling.

The electrically heated pads consist of strip conductors sandwiched between layers of Neoprene, or glass fibre cloth impregnated with epoxy resin. Some heaters are heated continuously, as an anti-icing system preventing the formation of ice on the leading edges, whilst other elements are heated intermittently.

The latter type of element are divided into sections by breaker strips which are heated continuously.

Fig.9-3 shows an electrically heated element assembly including the breaker strip type of installation.

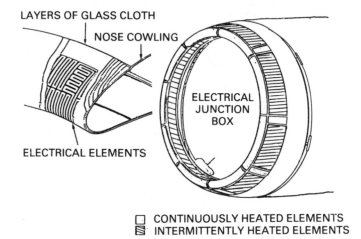

☐ CONTINUOUSLY HEATED ELEMENTS
▨ INTERMITTENTLY HEATED ELEMENTS

Fig.9-3. Electrically Heated Element Assembly.

9.6 Electrical Ice Protection Operation.

Electrical power is supplied by an AC Generator and to reduce the weight and size of the system, and in particular the generator, the de-icing electrical loads are cycled between the engine, propeller, and sometimes the airframe. It can be seen now referring again to Fig.9-3 that part of the cowling is heated continuously and part intermittently, this type of operation will assist in keeping the weight and size of the generator to a minimum.

In normal operation, the continuous heated elements prevent any ice forming, however, the intermittently heated elements allow ice to form, during their "heat off" cycle. During the heat on cycle ice that has adhered to the area will be removed, or allowed to break off due to the heating action of the elements coupled with the action of the airflow over the area.

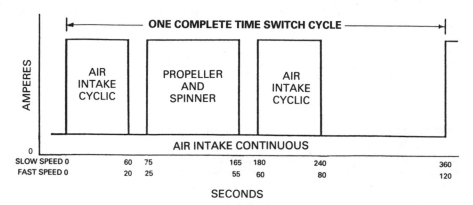

Fig.9-4. Cycle Sequence.

The continuously heated breaker strips limit the size of the area on which ice can form on the intermittently heated areas.

The cycling time of the intermittently heated elements is arranged to ensure that the engine will not be seriously effected by the amount of ice that may build up during the heat off period, and the heat on time is long enough to ensure any ice that has formed will be freed from the area.

A two speed system is often used to accommodate the propeller and spinner requirements, a fast cycle at higher atmospheric temperatures when the water concentration is usually greater, and a slow cycle when lower atmospheric temperatures prevail.

Fig.9-4 shows an example cycling sequence chart.

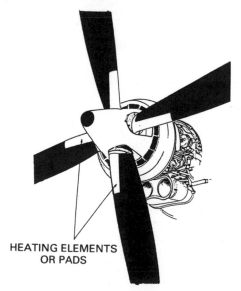

HEATING ELEMENTS
OR PADS

Fig.9-5. Electrically Heated Propeller Ice Protection.

Note: Most electrical ice protection systems are supplied by frequency wild generators in order to minimise weight and size.

9.7   Electrically Heated Propeller Ice Protection.

The propeller ice protection system is part of the main engine ice protection system, however, the heated elements that are attached to the leading edge of the propeller blades do not cover the full length of the blade. Firstly, the forces experienced toward the blade tip are such that to achieve satisfactory bonding of the heating elements to the blade is almost impossible, therefore, the heating element is confined to the root areas of the blade. Equally, toward the tip of the propeller blade an element of dynamic heating tends to prevent the formation of ice.

Fig.9-5 shows the location of the heating elements or pads on a typical turbo-prop propeller.

TEST YOURSELF 9
ICE PROTECTION SYSTEMS

1. Hot air for the purpose of ice protection systems is normally obtained from:
   - (a) heater elements.
   - (b) the low pressure stages of the compressor.
   - (c) the high pressure stages of the compressor.

   Ref. 9.4.

2. The air pressure in the heated air system of ice protection.
   - (a) the same as the engine compressor pressure.
   - (b) controlled by a pressure relief valve.
   - (c) controlled by a pressure regulator valve.

   Ref. 9.4.

3. The electrically heated ice protection system:
   - (a) heats air which is then ducted to specific areas.
   - (b) heats pads which are bonded to certain points.
   - (c) heats oil which is ducted to certain points.

   Ref. 9.5.

4. Ice is most likely to form:
   - (a) at low atmospheric temperatures.
   - (b) at high atmospheric temperatures.
   - (c) at any atmospheric temperature.

   Ref. 9.6.

5. Propeller ice protection pads are:
   - (a) heated by hot air.
   - (b) located toward the blade tip.
   - (c) located toward the blade root.

   Ref. 9.7.

10

ENGINE PERFORMANCE AND HANDLING

10.1 Introduction.

Different gas turbine engine types handle in different ways and the following is a guide to some of the more general features and problems. For specific data the particular engines manuals must be consulted.

10.2 Pre-Starting Precautions.

When at all possible the aircraft should be headed into wind during engine starting or for ground running. The area around the aircraft should be clear of all obstructions, loose equipment or any objects which may be drawn into the intake or damaged by the jet exhaust. It is very important that personnel in the vicinity of the aircraft are made aware of the engine's starting and/or running and advised to keep clear.

10.3 Starting.

On most aircraft the starting sequence of a gas turbine engine is automatic once engine start has been selected. On most aircraft gas turbine engines, prior to initiating the start sequence, the low pressure and high pressure fuel cocks must be turned ON, and the low pressure fuel pumps must be turned ON to allow a fuel flow to the engine driven, or high pressure, fuel pumps. Normally the throttle should be kept closed during the engine start sequence. On some installations protection devices prevent the start sequence being initiated unless the throttle is in the closed position. Failure to ensure the throttle is closed during the start sequence on many engines may result in over-fuelling of the engine.

When starting an engine with an electrical starting system the start button should be pushed in and held in for two to three seconds and then released. The starter sequence relay first will supply a low voltage current to drive the starter motor, then current to the booster coils for the ignition system igniters, and finally a high voltage current to the starter motor which then accelerates the engine at a great rate.

During the initial stages of engine acceleration the fuel pressure rises, the high pressure or engine driven fuel pumps will have moved to the "on load" or "on stroke" position when the engine was previously shut down and will now be delivering fuel under pressure to the engine. The fuel is sprayed into the combustion chambers from the burners and ignited either, on some older type engines, by the torch igniters, or high energy ignition units. On some installations the fuel pressure may rise too rapidly and fuel may be discharged into the combustion chambers before the engine rpm are high enough for a satisfactory light up, that is to say the air/fuel mixture will be incorrect, this situation may result in a "Hung" start.

A "Hung Start" will be indicated by the engine accelerating to a figure below "Idle" rpm and failing to accelerate any higher. In other words, the mixture is too rich. If this situation should occur with a fully automatic sequence start system, the engine must be "shut down" and a fresh attempt made to restart.

Note: A "Hung Start" is also known as a "Hot Start". ✗ WRONG!

On some engine installations, if a "Hung Start" situation is liable to occur, it is recommended the high pressure cock should be closed, or partially closed, at the commencement of the start sequence. This action will minimise the risk of an incorrect fuel/air ratio at the low initial rpm, possibly leading to overfuelling of the engine.

It should also be noted that at low engine rpm, an overfuelling situation as stated above, may possibly lead also to surging and an excessive engine gas temperature or jet pipe temperature.

After "light up", the engine speed increases under the combined influence of the turbine and starter motor. After approximately 30 seconds, the current to the starter motor (electric start system) and igniter units or plugs is automatically cut off and the engine becomes self sustaining.

The starting sequence should never be interrupted, that is to say, disconnected or switched off. Should this be done the start sequence continues, when re-connected, from the point it was stopped and this could result in flooding of the engine with fuel resulting in failure to start, and possibly damage to the start system and/or engine.

10.4 Failure of the Engine to Start.

In the event the engine fails to start, the high pressure fuel cock should be closed as soon as this becomes apparent. The action of closing the high pressure fuel cock will reduce the fuel flooding of the engine. The most likely cause of the start failure is insufficient electrical power to turn, or rotate, the engine at sufficient rpm. After closing the high pressure cock the engine should be allowed to run down and stop and sufficient time allowed for all surplus fuel to drain through the fuel drain valves. Time must be allowed for the starter motor to cool before any attempt is made to re-start the engine.

Note: Insufficient power on engine starting will also reduce the effectiveness of the igniters.

10.5 Wet Start.

Should an engine fail to start, as in the previous paragraph, the interior of the combustion chambers will be wet with fuel, fuel will have drained and collected in the bottom of the engine, some fuel may also have passed through the turbine and collected in the exhaust or jet pipe. In some instances the fuel drain valves will not allow all fuel to drain out of the engine. It is also possible that ignition during the first attempt to start did not take place effectively resulting in very little fuel actually being burned. If a normal start is now attempted and the accumulated fuel ignites an internal engine fire may result generating excessive temperatures and possible damage to the engine.

The resultant internal engine fire is sometimes termed "Torching". In the event an engine fails to start and excessive amounts of accumulated fuel in the engine are suspected, before a further attempt is made to start the engine, a "dry run" should be carried out. This is achieved by firstly ensuring the engine and starter motor have been given adequate time to cool, and as much fuel as possible has drained from the engine. The engine is then turned over by the starter motor with the high pressure cock, master starter switch, ignition, and all priming or booster pumps switched off, this will result in blowing air through the engine and thereby drying some of the accumulated fuel from the components in the engine prior to a further attempt to start the engine.

When a dry run is carried out, the starter motor must be given adequate time to cool before any further start sequence is initiated.

Note: It may be necessary to re-site the aircraft after an aborted "wet start" due to fuel that has drained from the aircraft will now constitute a serious fire hazard.

Although a dry run has been carried out to remove accumulations of fuel from the engine, often a degree of "torching" will take place at the second attempt to start the engine. Flames will be seen coming from the jet pipe, this will also be accompanied by a rise in engine gas temperature, usually however this will not be a serious problem provided the engine gas temperature remains within limits and no attempt is made to shut the engine down at this specific time.

10.6 Engine Resonance.

During starting of the engine, engine resonance may occur on light up and can be recognised by a rumbling sound from the engine. This situation usually occurs due to a degree of overfuelling, and may be overcome by partial closing of the high pressure fuel cock. As soon as the resonance subsides the high pressure fuel cock should be moved to the fully open position.

10.7 Immediately After Starting.

After the starting cycle is completed the engine should be allowed to idle for a brief period and the following should be checked:

(a) Oil Pressure.

(b) Burner or Fuel System Pressure.

(c) Engine Gas Temperature or Jet Pipe Temperature.

(d) All ancillary services.

(e) That All Relavent Instrumentation is operating satisfactorily.

10.8 Warming the Engine Up.

The engine must be allowed to warm up to its normal operating temperature which is carried out at ground idle rpm. Until the recommended operating temperature has been reached the throttle should not be moved. If any throttle adjustment is required then the throttle should be moved smoothly and slowly. Any rapid movements during this period may cause the engine to stall or surge.

10.9 Taxying.

Rapid and unnecessary frequent opening and closing of the throttle should be avoided while taxying, as such actions may lead to overfuelling which in turn may cause surging and resonance, this in turn will lead to increased engine gas temperature.

The initial response of the engine to throttle movement is generally slow, and considerable power may be required to initially start moving some larger types of aircraft, however once the aircraft starts to move the power required during taxying is relatively small.

Axial flow engines are, as stated in previous chapters, susceptible to compressor stall and surge, particularly at low engine rpm which can be considerably aggravated in cross wind conditions. The combination of low engine rpm and cross winds are likely to occur during taxying and as such it may be necessary to use a slightly higher rpm to reduce stall tendencies.

In extreme conditions the turning of the aircraft into wind to recover from engine stall may be the only answer. It is therefore essential to avoid rapid throttle movements in such situations. Should the engine stall, then the throttle must be closed slowly and then re-opened slowly to re-establish satisfactory airflow conditions through the engine and in particular the compressor, and on very rare occasions it is necessary to shut the engine down and the re-start.

10.10 Take Off.

As in the case of aircraft taxying in cross wind conditions and the danger of engine surge, during take off in cross wind conditions the situation is even more critical. Should engine stall or surge occur during take off engine power will be lost at a critcal time, the surge or stall could also lead to a "flame-out". Modern gas turbine engines are equipped with various aids to minimise the onset of engine stall and its related conditions, even so, every precaution must be taken to ensure any such situation does not arise. As engine rpm are increased for take off the throttle must be moved smoothly and slowly, the engine must be monitored to ensure there is not the slightest indication of the onset of surge or stall. Engine gas temperature must be correct, it must not be too high or indeed too low. Monitor to ensure such devices, discussed in previous chapters are functioning correctly. For take off Inlet Guide Vanes must be fully open, Intermediate Bleed Valves operating correctly, Variable Stators operating correctly, and rear or main Bleed Valves operating correctly.

Additionally, most modern aircraft require as further protection the Auxiliary Power Unit to be running during take off as an insurance against main generator supply failure, and the igniter system operating to give instant re-light in the event a flame out occurs.

10.11   Climbing.

If the correct climbing speeds are not used, and particularly if the speed is too low, the rate of climb is therefore reduced. At high altitudes, unless the correct speed is used the aircraft will not climb at all. During the climb at the recommended rpm and airspeed, a careful watch must be kept on the engine gas temperature which should not exceed the permitted maximum, the throttle being closed slightly if necessary.

Under certain conditions some engines are prone to surge while climbing at higher altitudes. With centrifugal compressor engines the symptom of a surge is a muffled detonation in the engine and to reduce or rectify the situation, the throttle should be closed slightly and/or the airspeed increased.

With an axial flow engine there may be indication of surge by a loud "cough" or "bang" from the engine or there may be no audible warning before the surge, the first symptom being a loss of power or a "flame out". If a sudden loss of power occurs the throttle must be closed immediately; if a flame out has also occurred then the high pressure fuel cock must be closed as well as the throttle. This type of surge normally only occurs if the climbing speed is lower than normal. If the climbing speed falls below the correct figure at high altitude power should be reduced below the climb rpm while the speed is restored by diving the aircraft until the correct speed is obtained.

In spite of the Barometric Pressure Control, the rpm for a given throttle setting may tend to increase with increase of altitude. With increase of altitude the atmosphere becomes less dense reducing the back pressure on the engine causing the engine rpm to increase while the thrust will reduce.

Therefore to maintain constant rpm the throttle should be progressively closed. More modern types of gas turbine with improved engine control systems have a reduced tendency for the rpm to vary with altitude for a given power setting.

10.12   General Handling.

The principles of handling the gas turbine engine are determined by the fact that it best operates at a fixed throttle setting. By design the engine consists of a matched set of primary components which are designed to give an optimum performance at a given throttle setting, therefore any deviation from such matched settings, such as low fuel/air ratio, excessively high mass flow at intake, will be a deviation from normal engine operation. It must also be appreciated that deviations from normal operation, such as, in pure principle, movement of the throttle, from the optimum setting will also be a deviation from normal operation. It must also be noted constant changes of the throttle setting will increase wear and therefore reduce the life of the engine.

Various devices, such as variable inlet guide vanes (Swirl Vanes), Barometric Pressure Control, Automatic Control Unit, Bleed Valves and others, are fitted to assist the pilot in maintaining a balanced control of the engine in changing the thrust condition. Even with such devices great care must be taken when operating the throttle, if such devices suffer a malfunction successful control of the engine can still be maintained but even greater attention must be paid to throttle handling and the preservation of a good flow in the compressor.

At high altitudes gas turbine engines become extremely sensitive to throttle movement and the range of movement between idling and full power may be very small due to:

(a) The lower limit which is dictated by the higher idling rpm required to provide adequate fuel pressure for combustion and/or cabin pressurising requirements.

(b) The upper limit dictated by the throttle position above which the rpm and/or engine gas temperature limits are exceeded.

Flame Out (flame extinction) may occur if the throttle is opened too rapidly. If the throttle is opened too rapidly this may result in a momentary increase in engine gas temperature followed by a flame out. If this happens, or if the engine is intentionally stopped in flight, the high pressure fuel cock should be closed immediately. Note should be made when relighting an engine at altitude the engine starter motor system should not normally be used as this may damage the engine, the airflow through the engine will normally give adequate rpm for relighting.

10.13 Centrifugal Compressor Engines.

With this type of engine there is little risk of flame extinction provided the throttle is moved smoothly and not too rapidly. The higher the altitude so the engine idling rpm increases, and the more sensitive the engine to throttle movement.

10.14 Axial Flow Type Engines.

If when the throttle is opened the rpm remains constant and the engine gas temperature rises to the maximum permitted level, the throttle should be closed fully immediately, these symptoms indicate surging or a stalled compressor condition exists. After the throttle has been fully closed the throttle may be opened again ensuring the throttle movement is kept slow, at the same time special attention must be paid to the engine gas temperature to ensure it remains within limits and a repeat surge or stall does not occur.

Low engine rpm should be avoided as much as possible, if however, the rpm has been allowed to drop below the flight minimum value, when the throttle setting is increased throttle movement must be carried out slowly, again due to the possibility of surge or stall in the compressor. Particular attention must be paid to this situation when on the approach when the airspeed is low and the aircraft is sinking in a nose up attitude which may cause the airflow to stall at the lips of the engine intakes. If the rpm is kept at or above the recommended value on the landing approach, until the decision to actually land has been made, such surge or stall conditions may be avoided.

Above 3000ft the effect of the Acceleration Control Unit is reduced on some engines, and any rapid acceleration of the engine causes overfuelling which may then lead to stalling or surging of the compressor. Engine acceleration characteristics deteriorate with increased altitude and care must be taken when increasing power at high altitudes, also care must be taken to avoid excessive engine gas temperature with or during acceleration.

10.15   High Altitude Surge.

Above 30,000 feet-40,000 feet, when flying at a low Indicated Airspeed and high rpm under very low temperatures, high altitude surge may occur. The risk of this type of surge can be avoided by keeping the rpm at the recommended value and minus 100 rpm for each 5 degrees below minus 55 degrees C.

10.16   Variable Position Inlet Guide Vanes
(Variable Position Swirl Vanes).

The action of the variable position inlet guide vanes have no noticeable effect on engine running, however, compressor efficiency is reduced unless the guide vanes move to the fully open position at the recommended engine rpm. On modern gas turbines this action is fully automatic. The lowest specific fuel consumption can only be obtained by operating with the variable inlet guide vanes fully open. Remember when engine starting the guide vanes should be in the fully closed position.

10.17   Mechanical Failure in Flight.

In the event mechanical failure occurs to the engine in flight the immediate action to be taken should be:

(a) Close the throttle and HP Cock.

(b) Switch off the LP Pumps, and if the failure is accompanied by a strong risk of fire, close the LP Fuel cocks also.

(c) In twin engined aircraft, shed all non-essential load and land the aircraft as soon as possible.

10.18   Engine Icing.

Centrifugal Compressor Engines do not encounter serious icing problems, this is mainly due to the combination of centrifugal force, temperature rise and rugged construction found in this type of gas turbine. The only conditions which will present a problem to this type is in the event severe icing is present.

Axial flow compressors are seriously affected by the same atmospheric conditions that cause airframe icing. Ice may form on the inlet guide vanes causing a restricted and turbulent airflow with a consequent loss in thrust and rise in engine gas temperature. Heavy icing can cause an excessive engine gas temperature leading to turbine and engine failure.

10.19   Effect of RPM on Rate of Icing.

For a given icing intensity the closer the spacing of the inlet guide vanes, the more serious the effect of icing. For a given engine the rate of ice accumulation is roughly proportional to the icing intensity and the mass airflow through the engine, i.e. to engine rpm. The rate of engine icing can therefore be reduced by decreasing the engine rpm.

10.20 Effect of True Air Speed on the Rate of Icing.

The rate of icing for a given icing index is almost constant up to 250 knots True Air Speed (TAS). At higher speeds, the rate of icing increases rapidly with increasing TAS. This phenomenon can be explained by the fact that the rate of engine icing is directly proportional to the liquid water content of the air gathered into the air intakes; the water content of the air in the intakes is not necessarily the same as that in the free airstream.

At low speeds, air is drawn into the intakes and at high speeds the air is rammed in, the transition speed, at which the pressure and temperature in the intake are atmospheric, is approximately 250 knots TAS. During the suction period the concentration of water content is virtually unchanged from that of the free airstream. At higher speeds above 250 knots, most of the suspended water droplets ahead of the projected area of the intake, tend to pass into the intake while some of the air in this same projected area is deflected round the intakes. The inertia of the droplets prevents them from being deflected and so the water content of the air in the intake is increased, therefore a reduction of TAS to 250 knots will reduce the rate of icing.

The reduced pressure caused by the compressor sucking air in the intake is at its lowest at zero speed. The pressure drop also increases with raise in rpm. The pressure drop is, of course, accompanied by a temperature drop. On the ground, or at very low speeds and high rpm air at ambient temperature will be reduced to sub freezing temperatures as it enters the intake, and any water content would therefore freeze onto the inlet guide vanes. The suction temperature drop which occurs is of the order of 5° C to 10° C. This temperature drop occurs at high rpm at the lowest altitudes and decreases with decreasing rpm or increasing TAS. Under these conditions visible moisture is needed to form icing, therefore take off in fog, at temperatures slightly above freezing, may result in ice forming.

Anti-icing systems and De-icing systems are discussed in previous chapters.

10.21 Approach and Landing, Turbojet Engines.

With turbojet engines, approach should be made under power to ensure a quick response for additional thrust is available if it becomes necessary to adjust the glide path by use of the throttle. For specific aircraft, minimum engine rpm are recommended for approach configurations. The rpm should be kept at or above this figure until the decision to land has been made and the runway can be seen. In the event the landing is aborted and the decision is made to go round again any movement of the throttle should be made smoothly to maximum power to avoid surge.

If the decision has been made to go round again after touch down and the engine rpm has reduced below the recommended approach rpm the throttle must be opened very carefully until the minimum approach rpm is reached or the engine will surge. When the throttle is opened up under these conditions the engine takes longer to accelerate to full power.

10.22   Stopping the Engine.

The engine must not be shut down, or stopped, until the engine temperature has reduced to the recommended figure. Normally after touch down, and the aircraft has taxied in, the engine is cool enough to be stopped. Although slight variations in procedure exist with different engine and aircraft types, generally the throttle must be fully closed and the high pressure fuel cock turned off. If however the temperatures are above the recommended values, the engine should be run at approximately twice the idling rpm for a short period to allow the engine to cool. The engine throttle should then be closed and the engine allowed to idle for approximately 30 seconds and then the high pressure cock closed, or turned off. The engine continues to run for several minutes until combustion has ceased and the engine has run down. The low pressure fuel cock should not be turned off until the engine has stopped turning. If the low pressure cock is turned off prior to the engine stopping the high pressure fuel pump will be run dry and air will be drawn into the system resulting in the system requiring to be re-primed with fuel and bled. It should also be noted, in the event the low pressure cock is turned off before the high pressure cock when stopping the engine, the run down time of the engine will be increased as well as the system being allowed to run dry.

10.23   Relighting Turbojet Engines.

In the event of a flame out, or flame extinction, occurs in flight a relighting of the engine, providing there is no mechanical or system failure, is normally possible on modern gas turbine engines. With some engines relighting is possible up to 35,000 feet, in most cases much lower altitudes are recommended and generally the lower the altitude the greater the degree of success.

If flame out occurs the following actions should be taken:

(a) Close the high pressure fuel cock immediately to prevent the accumulation of fuel in the engine which would make relighting much more difficult.

(b) Fly at the recommended relighting indicated air speed and altitude.

(c) Ensure that at least one low pressure fuel cock and booster pump are on, that the fuel pressure warning light is out, and that there is enough fuel in the selected fuel tanks.

(d) Switch on the relight and emergency booster pump if fitted.

(e) Set the throttle to the recommended position. This will vary with aircraft types, as experience has shown that, while some engines relight more readily with the throttle in the fully closed position others relight more effectively with the throttle partially open.

(f) Ensure that the master starting switch and ignition switch, if fitted are in the on position.

(g) Press the relight button and open the high pressure fuel cock to the fully open position.

(h) Immediately a rise in rpm or engine gas temperature is indicated, release the relight button and close the throttle. The engine should then accelerate to idle rpm for the altitude and may then be opened up slowly to the desired figure.

10.24 Gas Turbine Engine Ratings.

Introduction.

Generally engines of the turbojet type are rated in pounds of thrust developed, and this in turn is divided into specific thrust ratings for specific functions. Broadly they are as follows:

(a) Takeoff Rated Thrust.

(b) Maximum Continuous.

(c) Maximum Climb.

(d) Maximum Cruise.

(e) Idle.

For practical purposes normally the engine rating is interpreted in terms of engine pressure ratio (EPR) or on some engines, mostly military, by a specific throttle setting.

(a) Takeoff Rated Thrust.

Will normally be obtained at a throttle setting below the full forward position and may be sub-divided into two categories:

Takeoff (Wet)

This is the maximum takeoff thrust certified for engines that use water injection. The rating is selected by operating the water injection system and setting the throttle to obtain the computed "Wet" Takeoff Thrust in terms of engine pressure ratio. This rating is restricted normally to takeoff, is time limited, and has altitude and ambient air or water limitations.

Takeoff (Dry)

This is the maximum thrust certified without water injection. The rating is selected by setting the throttle to obtain the computed Takeoff (Dry) thrust in terms of engine pressure ratio for the prevailing conditions of ambient temperature and barometric pressure. The rating is time limited, and is used only for takeoff, and as required, for Reverse Thrust when landing.

(b) Maximum Continuous.

This thrust rating is the maximum thrust certified for continuous use and is normally only used at the discretion of the pilot or to ensure safe flight.

(c) Maximum Climb.

This is the maximum thrust approved for normal climb. The rating is obtained by adjusting the throttle to obtain a predetermined engine pressure ratio. On some engines, Maximum Continuous and Maximum Climb thrust are the same.

(d) Maximum Cruise.

This is the maximum thrust approved for cruise flight conditions and is obtained in the same manner as Maximum Continuous and Maximum Climb thrust.

(e) Ground Idle.

Ground Idle is the minimum thrust at which the engine must be operated at specific ground or flight conditions when the throttle lever is placed in the ground idle position.

Commercial engines are part throttle engines, that is, rated thrust is obtained at less than full throttle position. Taking their name from the shape of the takeoff thrust curve, the so called part throttle engines are also known as "Flat Rated" engines.

Note: Details of the handling of Turboprop engines are dealt with in the volume on "Aircraft Propellers" in this series of books.

TEST YOURSELF 10
ENGINE PERFORMANCE AND HANDLING

1. A gas turbine engine, on starting, accelerates to a figure below idle rpm and fails to accelerate above that value, this indicates:
   (a) a wet start.
   – (b) a hung start.
   (c) a surge condition.

   Ref. 10.3.

2. When the gas turbine engine is shut down, the high pressure fuel pump:
   (a) will move to the off load position.
   (b) will remain at the setting it is in at time of shut down.
   – (c) will move to the on load position.

   Ref. 10.3.

3. Prior to engine starting, the throttle:
   (a) must be set at ground idle.
   (b) must be set at a value above ground idle.
   – (c) must be closed.

   Ref. 10.3.

4. If an engine fails to start, the:
   (a) high pressure cock should be closed when the engine has stopped.
   (b) high pressure cock should be closed as soon as ignition is switched off.
   – (c) high pressure cock should be closed as soon as failure to start becomes apparent.

   Ref. 10.4.

5. On some engine types, resonance may be reduced, during starting by:
   (a) increasing the throttle setting.
   (b) fully closing the high pressure cock.
   – (c) partially closing the high pressure cock.

   Ref. 10.6.

6. Torching is a term sometimes used to describe:
    (a) the point of ignition on engine starting.
    (b) the re-light after a flame out.
    — (c) an internal engine fire.

Ref. 10.5.

7. Variable inlet guide vanes:
    — (a) must be fully open on engine starting.
    (b) may be in any mid position on engine starting.
    (c) must be fully closed on engine starting.

Ref. 10.16.

8. If, when stopping the gas turbine, the low pressure fuel cock is closed first:
    — (a) the engine run down time will increase.
    (b) the engine run down time will be unaffected.
    (c) the engine run down time will be reduced.

Ref. 10.22.

9. In the event a surge is suspected in the compressor of a gas turbine engine, the:
    (a) throttle must be opened slowly.
    (b) engine must be shut down.
    — (c) throttle must be closed slowly.

Ref. 10.14.

10. On most aircraft fitted with gas turbine engines, prior to engine shut down, if the engine temperatures are too high:
    — (a) the engine must be run at idle rpm until it cools down.
    (b) the engine must be run at approximately twice idle rpm until it cools.
    (c) the fuel/air mixture must be moved to rich.

Ref. 10.22.

11

GAS TURBINE CONTROLS AND INSTRUMENTATION

11.1 Introduction.

This chapter is intended to give the reader a basic knowledge of the general controls and instruments to be found in the cockpit of the average aircraft relating to the gas turbine engine. Controls and instrumentation vary from one aircraft type to another, below are listed most of the primary controls and instruments to be found.

11.2 Engine and Engine System Controls.

(a) Throttle Lever.
   Selects the engine fuel flow and hence controls the engine speed. Normally mounted between the pilot's seats on the main control quadrant. See Fig.11-1.

(b) High Pressure Fuel Cock (HP Cock).
   Sometimes termed the High Pressure Shut Off Cock, provides a means of stopping the engine in that it starves the engine of fuel when closed.

(c) Low Pressure Fuel Cock (LP Cock).
   Normally controlled by an electric actuator which in turn is operated by a switch in the cockpit. This is essentially an on/off control for the fuel system from the fuel tank, or tanks, to the High Pressure Pump. Switches are also provided for transfer pumps to enable fuel to be controlled between tank.

(d) Thrust Reversal.
   This normally takes the form of a separate lever which gives instinctive control of engine power during reverse thrust operation.

(e) Reheat.
   Reheat, or afterburning, is controlled by a lever in the cockpit. On most modern aircraft the variable exhaust or propelling nozzle is controlled automatically.

11.3 Gas Turbine Instrumentation.

Although engine installations may differ, depending upon the type of both the aircraft and the engine, gas turbine engine control will usually be obtained by the use of the following instrumentation. Engine thrust indication will be dealt with separately.

(a) **Tachometer** — Engine rotor rpm may be sensed by a mechanically-driven tachometer generator, mechanically-driven permanent magnet, or a pulse pick-up which senses passing compressor of fan blades or passing gear teeth. The output or signal from any of the above sensors is directed to an appropriate indicator in the cockpit, the indicator being calibrated to read directly in per cent rpm. A remote readout instrument in the aircraft is calibrated to read directly in per cent rpm. Dual axial flow compressor engines are usually provided with two tachometers, one tachometer indicating low pressure compressor speed (N_1), the other indicating high pressure compressor speed (N_2).

For most axial flow compressor engines, the main purpose of the tachometer is to monitor rpm during an engine start and to indicate an overspeed condition, should one occur. Although Pratt & Whitney does not recommend the use of the tachometer for setting thrust on axial flow compressor engines, the low pressure compressor (N_1) tachometer on EPR-controlled dual compressor engines may be used as an approximate reference for setting engine thrust in transient and certain other flight conditions. Whenever the N_1 tachometer is used to set engine thrust, the thrust setting should be more accurately adjusted by means of engine pressure ratio just as soon as possible. On single compressor axial flow engines, it is strongly recommended that engine speed not be used as a primary means of setting or checking engine thrust. Refer to the discussion under Engine Thrust Indication which follows.

(b) **Exhaust Gas Temperature Indicator** — Turbine engines may be instrumented for exhaust gas temperature indication at locations before, between, or behind the turbine stages. Exhaust gas temperature is an engine operating limit, and is used to monitor the mechanical integrity of the turbines, as well as to check engine operating conditions. Actually, the temperature at the turbine inlet is the important consideration, this being the most critical of all of the engine variables. However, as has been pointed out, it is impractical to measure turbine inlet temperature in most engines. Consequently, thermocouples are inserted at the turbine discharge instead, this temperature providing a relative indication of that at the inlet. Although the temperature at this point is much lower than that at the inlet, it enables the pilot to maintain surveillance over engine internal operating conditions.

Several thermocouples are usually used, spaced at intervals around the perimeter of the engine exhaust duct near the turbine exit. The exhaust gas temperature indicator in the aircraft shows the average of the temperatures measured by the individual thermocouples. The readings of the several thermocouples can also usually be obtained individually during ground engine maintenance by the use of a selective switch. The spread between the lowest and the highest thermocouple reading is useful in maintenance because it serves to indicate the presence of hot or cold spots in the engine exhaust pattern which may mean that something is wrong inside the engine. Because the importance of exhaust gas temperature cannot be over-emphasised, the subject is discussed in more detail in Section V.

(c)  **Fuel Flow Indicator** — The fuel flow indicator shows the fuel flow in pounds (or kilograms) per hour to the fuel nozzles. Fuel flow is of fundamental interest for monitoring inflight fuel consumption, for checking engine performance, and for inflight cruise control. The relationship of abnormal fuel flow to the readings of the other instruments will provide one of the best indications as to the probable cause of an engine malfunction.

(d)  **Oil Pressure Indicator** — To guard against engine failures resulting from inadequate lubrication and cooling of the various engine parts, the oil supply to critical areas must be monitored. The oil pressure indicator shows the pressure relayed by the oil pressure transmitter. On most installations, the oil pressure transmitter takes breather pressure into consideration, relaying the true pressure drop across the oil jets in the oil system.

(e)  **Oil-In Temperature Indicator** — The ability of the engine oil to perform its job of lubricating and cooling is a function of the temperature of the oil, as well as the amount of oil supplied to the critical areas. An oil inlet temperature indicator is frequently provided to show the temperature of the oil as it enters the engine bearing compartments. Oil inlet temperature also serves as an indication of proper operation of the engine oil cooler.

(f)  **Fuel Inlet Pressure Indicator** — Fuel system characeristics frequenty make it advisable to monitor the fuel pump inlet pressure. In case of fuel flow stoppage in flight, it is desirable to locate the source of the difficulty quickly, in order to determine whether trouble has developed in the engine or in the aircraft fuel system, so that prompt corrective action may be taken. In addition, the fuel pump inlet pressure will indicate possible cavitation at the fuel pump inlet in flight, and will show whether or not the fuel system is operating properly during engine ground checks.

(g) **Air Temperature Indicator** — The air temperature indications currently used in aircraft are free air temperature (FAT), outside (OAT), ram (RAT), total (TAT) and static air temperature (SAT). Regardless of which temperature is instrumented in a specific aircraft model, the Flight Manual will show how to use it, in conjunction with applicable charts or tables, to set the EPR values which provide rated thrust levels. The

EPR setting varies with the thrust level desired and with the true total air temperature existing at the front of the engine. (T_{t2}). Some aircraft have instrumentation which indicates T_{t2} values that may be used without correction to determine EPR settings.

Except for an indicator to measure engine thrust, the above represents the minimum instrumentation considered adequate for control of the engine. Some installations may have additional instruments.

(h) **Engine Thrust Indication.**
The subject of the means by which a pilot sets and monitors the thrust produced by the engines installed in this aircraft has been mentioned a number of times in the foregoing text. The following repeats what has been said earlier while discussing thrust indication in detail.

  On some engines, engine rpm and exhaust gas temperature (EGT), together, are used for indicating and setting thrust on an engine installed in an aircraft. On such engines, the full rated thrust of the engine for takeoff is obtained by the pilot at 100 per cent rpm and a specified EGT. The specified EGT at 100 per cent rpm is established on a thrust-measuring ground test stand by varying the exhaust nozzle area of the engine as necessary to achieve the desired EGT.

 Aircraft centrifugal compressor engines, on some types, thrust is indicated by rpm, alone, and full rated thrust for takeoff is obtained when the tachometer reads 100 per cent.

 Most afterburning and non-afterburning aircraft turbojets and turbofans, both military and commercial, with single or dual axial flow compressors use engine pressure ratio (EPR) as a measure of engine thrust. EPR indicators compare the total turbine discharge pressure to the total pressure of the air entering the compressor, then indicate the ratio of these pressures. Engines instrumented for EPR have a fixed exhaust nozzle area. Two fixed areas are used on afterburning engines, one for non-afterburning operation and one for afterburning operation.

For engines with a fixed nozzle area, the actual exhaust gas temperatures obtained during operation are usually below the prescribed limits, as shown by Fig.11-1. Although it is permissible for an engine to operate at the temperature limit for any given thrust rating, an engine that does may have something wrong which causes the engine to run abnormally hot.

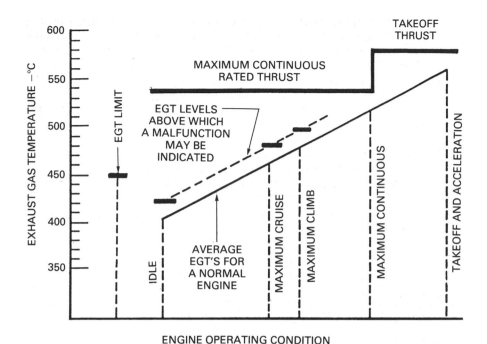

Fig.11-1. Exhaust Gas Temperature Limits for Typical Commercial Engine.

With the exception noted in the discussion pertaining to the use of the tachometer, engine rpm is considered a very inadequate parameter for setting and checking engine thrust on single and dual axial flow compressor turbojet and turbofan engines having fixed exhaust nozzle areas. Many complications arise when rpm is utilised as the controlling variable on such engines. The most important of these are listed below.

(i)   Since the high pressure compressor rpm on dual axial flow compressor engines, or the rpm of the whole compressor on single axial flow compressor engines, is governed by the fuel control, rpm does not provide an accurate means of determining whether or not the complete engine is functioning properly. As an example, rpm will not enable an engine operator to detect a damaged or dirty compressor unless rpm is carefully used in conjunction with other engine variables such as fuel flow, exhaust gas temperature, and engine pressure ratio.

(ii) Because the engines are "trimmed" by a fuel control adjustment to produce full rated thrust at a fixed throttle position on a standard day, rpm for any given thrust condition will vary slightly among individual engines, depending upon the engine trim speed. The variation in rpm must be taken into consideration whenever rpm is used to measure the thrust being developed by the

117

engine. This introduces a complication which cannot be tolerated whenever precise thrust settings are necessary during flight.

(iii) On dual axial flow compressor engines, one per cent variation in rpm results in approximately four per cent variation in thrust at the higher thrust settings for the low pressure compressor rotor (N_1), and five per cent variation for the high pressure compressor rotor (N_2), whereas one per cent variation in turbine discharge pressure or engine pressure ratio results in only one and one half per cent variation in thrust. The five per cent variation in thrust for one per cent variation in rpm also holds true for single axial flow compressor engines.

(iv) Rpm does not vary in direct proportion to the thrust being produced by the engine over the entire thrust range.

For these reasons, some manufacturers recommend that turbine discharge pressure or engine pressure ratio be used as the engine variable for indicating thrust on axial flow compressor engines with fixed area exhaust nozzles. The use of either of these is not only much simpler under most conditions than the use of rpm for engines of this type, but is considerably more accurate as well.

11.4 Instrumentation for Measuring Thrust (and Power for Turboprops)

For engines other than those using fully variable exhaust nozzles, turbine discharge pressure or engine pressure ratio can be used with good results to indicate or set engine thrust because they vary proportionally to the thrust the engine is developing. Most turbojet- and turbofan-powered aircraft today are instrumented for engine pressure ratio, and this is the parameter generally used to set or measure engine thrust during takeoff, climb and cruise. For very accurate thrust measurement, such as during ground trimming of an engine, turbine discharge pressure is often employed to measure thrust. In such cases, it is common practice to temporarily connect a turbine discharge pressure indicator to the engine for the duration of the engine trim run.

This is how the two methods of engine pressure measurement function:

Turbine Discharge Pressure Indicator — This instrument indicates the internal engine pressure upstream of the jet nozzle, immediately aft of the last stage of the turbine (P_{t5} or P_{t7}), and serves as an indication of the pressure available across the nozzle to generate thrust. Turbine discharge pressure must be used in conjunction with T_{t2} and P_{t2}, as will be explained later.

11.5 Engine Pressure Ratio Indicator —

This instrument indicates the engine pressure ratio as a measure of the thrust being developed by the engine. This is the ratio of the turbine discharge total pressure to the equivalent of the compressor inlet total

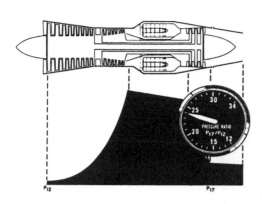

pressure (P_{t5}/P_{t2} or P_{t7}/P_{t2}). Values for P_{t2} must be corrected for inlet duct loss on the engine pressure ratio curves or charts by the aircraft manufacturer. Therefore, both for static (i.e. takeoff) and flight use, the actual value for P_{t2} will vary among different aircraft types and models because of installation effects. However, the relation of P_{t2} at the engine face to both P_{am} for static conditions and for P_{am} plus P_r (the pressure due to ram) in flight is determined during early, aircraft flight testing for each aircraft model, and is used thereafter as the reference pressure for P_{t5}/P_{t2} for P_{t7}/P_{t2}. The true (field) barometric pressure on the takeoff runway is P_{am}, and P_{am} plus P_r is equivalent to total pressure at, or near, the compressor inlet when airborne. Because it is inadvisable to instrument the compressor inlet directly for P_{t2}, the P_{t2} sense for the pressure ratio indicator may be placed at some other location on the aircraft, preferably as near the engine air inlet as possible. When the appropriate corrections have been made to the inflight charts in the aircraft Flight or Operation Manual, any rated thrust, or per cent of rated thrust, in terms of engine pressure ratio may be set with the aircraft throttle as a function of the total air temperature of T_{t2}.

Because the thrust developed by the engine is indicated by the pressure ratio between the pressure at the engine air inlet and the discharge pressure at the jet nozzle, turbine discharge pressure, by itself, should not be used directly as an accurate indication of the engine output. Compressor inlet pressure (P_{t2}) must be taken into account on curves or charts whenever turbine discharge pressure, alone, is instrumented on the aircraft. For static engine operation, this will usually be accomplished by showing barometric pressure, corrected for inlet duct loss, rather than P_{t2} values on the curves or charts. Inflight, curves or tables will usually show airspeed and altitude which will eliminate the need for virtually delineating P_{t2} values in the operating data. Engine pressure ratio indicators have the P_{t2} value introduced into the system, automatically taking this factor into account on the observed instrument reading.

Torquemeter (Turboprop Engines) — Because only a small part of the propulsive force produced by a turboprop is due to jet thrust, neither turbine discharge pressure nor engine pressure ratio is used to indicate the power being produced by the engine. Instead, a torquemeter is employed to measure the level of power that the engine is developing both on the ground and in flight. As the method of measuring torque varies, the engine Maintenance Manual should be consulted for a description of the manner in which a particular torquemeter system functions. In most systems, however, torquemeter oil pressure is used to actuate a torque indicating instrument in the aircraft. The torquemeter instrument portrays torquemeter oil pressure (which is proportional to engine power) in pounds per square inch (psi). Some torquemeter instruments are calibrated to read in terms of pound-feet (lb-ft) of torque, and some may read in shaft horsepower (SHP), directly.

11.6 Related Terms.

c_p, c_v	— Specific heats at constant pressure and volume
C	— Coefficient or constant
ESHP	— Equivalent shaft horsepower (turboprop)
ESFC	— Equivalent specific fuel consumption (turboprop)
F_g	— Gross thrust (lbs)
F_{11}	— Net thrust (lbs)
g	— Acceleration due to gravity, and mass conversion factor, 32.174
k, γ	— Gamma – ratio of specific heats (c_p, c_v)
M	— Mach number (velocity or airspeed divided by the speed of sound at the appropriate air temperature)
N	— Compressor speed (rpm or per cent) for a single compressor engine
N_1	— Speed (rpm or per cent) of the low pressure compressor of a dual compressor engine, or the compressor speed (rpm or per cent) of a single compressor engine equipped with a free turbine.
N_2	— Speed (rpm or per cent) of the high pressure compressor of a dual compressor engine, or the free turbine speed (rpm or per cent) of a single compressor engine equipped with a free turbine.
N_3	— Free turbine speed (rpm or per cent) of a dual compressor engine equipped with a free turbine.

NOTE: The symbols, N_g and N_f, are sometimes used to represent rpm for a free-turbine-type, turboprop or turboshaft engine. N_g is the symbol for the speed of the basic engine, or gas generator. N_f is the speed of the free turbine, or power turbine, as it is often called.

P	— Absolute pressure (gauge pressure plus atmospheric pressure – psia)
p	— Gauge pressure (psig)
T	— Absolute temperature (°R or °K)
t	— Temperature (°F or °C)
V	— Velocity (usually in ft/sec)
v	— Volume (in appropriate units)
W	— Weight (usually in lbs)
w	— Rate of flow (gas, such as air, or liquid, such as fuel, usually in lbs/sec or lbs/hr)
Δ (Delta)	— Difference or change (i.e. ΔP represents a pressure difference, such as one between the two sides of a fuel filter)

δ (Delta)   — Standard correction factor for pressure (relative absolute pressure)

η (Eta)   — Efficiency

θ (Theta)   — Standard correction factor for temperature (relative absolute temperature)

ρ (Rho)   — Density

The subscripts used with a number of the above letters and symbols more accurately define the quantity in each case. The Engine Station subscripts listed below simply show at what point in the engine each quantity is being taken. For example, P_{t2} means total (t) absolute pressure (P) taken at Station 7 in the engine.

12

GAS TURBINE DEVELOPMENTS

12.1 Introduction.

Constant demand for greater efficiency, economy and quieter engines has produced a number of variations of the basic turbojet gas turbine powerplant. In this chapter some of the more widely used variations are explained.

12.2 Ducted Fan Engines.

The ducted fan engine has been developed to increase propulsive efficiency by decreasing the mean speed of the exhaust gases and at the same time increasing the total mass flow. Further energy is taken from the main gas flow to drive an additional turbine coupled to a fan running in an annular duct. The fan compresses air taken from a separate atmospheric source to provide a cold jet of greater mass flow and comparatively low speed. The cold jet is then fed into the hot jet at the propelling nozzle, or may join the hot gases aft of the propelling nozzle, thus reducing the temperature and raising the overall mass flow through the engine and, consequently, the engine efficiency.

Fig.12-1 shows an example layout of a ducted fan engine.

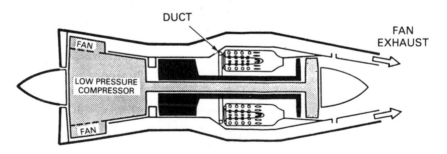

Fig.12-1. Ducted Fan Engine.

The fan may be fitted at the front of the engine or at the rear, or hot, end.

12.3 Bypass Engines.

The Bypass engine also uses separate cold and hot streams in its operation. After leaving the compressor, the air is split into two flows, a primary flow which passes through the engine in the normal way, and a secondary flow which bypasses the combustion zone to flow around the engine and rejoin the hot jet at the jet nozzle. The amount of by-passed air is smaller than the primary flow. The propulsive efficiency is higher than in the pure turbojet, since the cold bypass air reduces the temperature and increases the mass flow.

Fig.12-2 shows an example of a bypass engine layout.

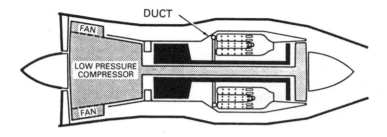

Fig.12-2. By-pass Gas Turbine.

12.4 Turbo-Fan or Ducted Fan With Short Ducts.

This type of engine is widely used on modern airliners and couples high efficiency with reduced noise levels.

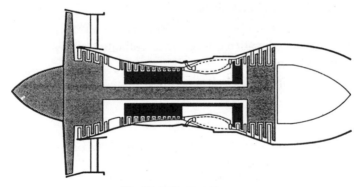

Fig.12-3. Turbo-Fan.

PRACTICE PAPER 1

1. On leaving the compressor, the air:
   - (a) passes into the primary zone of the combustion chamber.
   - (b) passes through the diffuser.
   - (c) passes into the primary and secondary zone of the combustion chamber.
   - (d) passes into the swirl assembly of the combustion chamber.

   Ref. Ch. 1 Para 1.3

2. Fuel on entering the combustion chamber is primarily atomised by:
   - (a) the swirl vanes.
   - (b) the diffuser.
   - (c) the dilution holes.
   - (d) the burner feed.

   Ref. Ch. 1 Para 1.3

3. The diffuser after the compressor:
   - (a) converts the velocity energy into pressure energy.
   - (b) converts the pressure energy into velocity energy.
   - (c) straightens the airflow.
   - (d) creates a swirl effect in the airflow.

   Ref. Ch. 1 Para 1.3

4. In a basic turbojet engine, of the total energy produced, approximately:
   - (a) 60% leaves the engine as thrust.
   - (b) 40% leaves the engine as thrust.
   - (c) 90% leaves the engine as thrust.
   - (d) 25% leaves the engine as thrust.

   Ref. Ch. 1 Para 1.3

5. At subsonic speeds, a turbojet engine requires:
   - (a) a convergent intake.
   - (b) a variable intake.
   - (c) a convergent/divergent intake.
   - (d) a divergent intake.

   Ref. Ch. 1 Para 1.8

6. The compressor is:
    (a) rotated by free stream air.
    (b) driven by the inlet guide vanes.
    (c) driven by an electric motor.
    (d) driven by the turbine.

Ref. Ch. 1   Para 1.3

7. A basic centrifugal compressor, generally produces a pressure ratio of:
    (a) 4 to 4.5 to one.
    (b) 30 to one.
    (c) 130 to one.
    (d) 15 to one.

Ref. Ch. 2   Para 2.4

8. Modern centrifugal compressors produce a balance of air compression between that done by the impeller, and that done by the diffuser is approximately:
    (a) 20% to 80%.
    (b) 40% to 60%.
    (c) 50% to 50%.
    (d) 10% to 90%.

Ref. Ch. 2   Para 2.5

9. Double sided, Double entry centrifugal compressors:
    (a) have additional efficiency loss due to heat transfers through the disc or shroud.
    (b) are more difficult to balance.
    (c) are less efficient due to limited rpm.
    (d) have additional efficiency loss due to reduced operating.

Ref. Ch. 2   Para 2.5

10. The compressor blades of an axial flow compressor are curved throughout their length and:
    (a) their angle of incidence increases from root to tip.
    (b) their angle of incidence reduces from root to tip.
    (c) their angle of attack reduces from root to tip.
    (d) their angle of attack increases from root to tip.

Ref. Ch. 2   Para 2.9

11. The compression ratio of the compressor:
    (a) is the measure of air pressure between each stage.
    (b) is the measure of air pressure between the diffuser and combustion chambers.
    (c) is the measure of air pressure between compressor inlet and compressor outlet.
    (d) is the measure of air pressure between free stream pressure and compressor outlet.
                                                    Ref. Ch. 2   Para 2.10

12. Compressor surge may be minimised by use of:
    (a) fixed inlet guide vanes.
    (b) compressor bleed.
    (c) Turbo-fans.
    (d) swirl vanes.
                                                    Ref. Ch. 2   Para 2.14

13. Air release valves, in the compressor of a gas turbine, are opened:
    (a) automatically.
    (b) manually by the pilot.
    (c) only to supply cabin conditioning when required.
    (d) only after the engine is above ground idle rpm.
                                                    Ref. Ch. 2   Para 2.17

14. When starting a twin spool compressor engine:
    (a) both spools are rotated to avoid surge.
    (b) the low pressure spool is rotated first to avoid surge.
    (c) the high pressure spool is rotated first to avoid surge.
    (d) the free turbine only is rotated to avoid surge.
                                                    Ref. Ch. 2   Para 2.18

15. Turbine blade tip turbulence:
    (a) may be reduced by blade creep.
    (b) may be reduced by disc shrouding.
    (c) may be reduced by blade tip shrouding.
    (d) may be reduced by fir tree shrouding.
                                                    Ref. Ch. 4   Para 4.5

16. Blade creep is:
    (a) reduced by tip shrouding.
    (b) a permanent lengthening of the blade.
    (c) a temporary lengthening of the blade.
    (d) reduced by disc shrouding.
                                                    Ref. Ch. 4   Para 4.7

17. The main bearings of the compressor/turbine drive shaft are mounted via:
    (a) needle roller bearings.
    (b) nylon bearings.
    (c) ball bearings.
    — (d) ball or roller bearings.

    Ref. Ch. 4   Para 4.4

18. Reverse thrust power available is:
    (a) 90%.
    (b) 100%.
    — (c) 50%.
    (d) 25%.

    Ref. Ch. 4c   Para 4c.3

19. Reverse thrust is directed:
    (a) completely in the opposite direction to normal flow.
    (b) at 90 degrees to the relative airflow.
    — (c) at 45 degrees to the relative airflow.
    (d) at 15 degrees to the relative airflow.

    Ref. Ch. 4c   Para 4c.3

20. Ice is prevented from:
    (a) blocking the HP filter by pre heating the fuel
    — (b) blocking the LP filter by pre heating the fuel.
    (c) forming in the fuel by pre heating the fuel tank.
    (d) blocking the LP filter by pre heating the filter element.

    Ref. Ch. 5   Para 5.2